UFOLOGY

UFOLOGY

James M. McCampbell

CELESTIAL ARTS
Millbrae, California

CELESTIAL ARTS
231 Adrian Road
Millbrae, California 94030

First Printing, September 1976
Made in the United States of America

Library of Congress Cataloging in Publication Data

McCampbell, James M
    UFOlogy.

    Includes bibliographical references.
    1. Flying saucers.   I. Title.
TL789.M15 1976   001.9'42   73-93488
ISBN: 0-89087-144-2

    2 3 4 5 6 7 — 81 80 79 78 77

CONTENTS

ACKNOWLEDGMENTS

The opportunity to study Unidentified Flying Objects at all is simply a gift from the witnesses; we would be totally ignorant on this subject without their accounts. I am grateful that many thousands of people who saw something strange in the sky were not afraid to tell somebody about their experiences. I am further indebted to the many researchers who have diligently investigated the individual sightings and shared their findings in various publications. These sources of information are carefully cited throughout the text. The literature on UFOs, however, is so extensive that it has not been possible to pinpoint and credit all authors who may have influenced my thinking. Their contributions must come under a blanket acknowledgment that is equally sincere. No slight is intended to writers who have been ignored, even though their works may be well-known and significant.

I am grateful to the artist, Hal Crawford, for his excellent illustration that is used with the kind permission of Hayden C. Hewes, Director, International UFO Bureau, P. O. Box 1281, Oklahoma City, Oklahoma 73103.

The many frustrations of writing a book in a perplexing field were greatly mollified by Mrs. Judy Vilar whose spirit remained bright as she typed untold numbers of final drafts that, alas, proved to be only preliminary.

Also deserving of thanks are my wife, Carol, grown children, Ann, Kathy, and Nancy, and, rounding out the household while attending college in the U.S., Miss Gunilla Bexar from Finland. They pretended not to notice that the old man went crackers and started talking a lot about flying saucers and other improbable things, even enduring his snippy demeanor when progress was too slow.

For as God was the help of our reason to illuminate us, so should we likewise turn it every way, that we may be more capable of understanding His mysteries; provided only that the mind be enlargened, according to its capacity, to the grandeur of the mysteries, and not the mysteries contracted to the narrowness of the mind.

— *Francis Bacon*

PREFACE

Very few subjects have attracted as much attention throughout the world as Unidentified Flying Objects. Nearly everyone in the civilized world has at least heard of them. Even some natives beyond the reach of modern communications have described things in the sky that fit the definition. Beyond that, however, there is little unanimity. Every individual has naturally formed his own opinion on the topic, and beliefs vary greatly. Most reasonable people would accept a full and convincing proof of the identity of these mysterious objects. UFOs remain controversial, however, because no attempt at explaining the phenomenon has been entirely successful.

The fundamental fact confronting us is the existence of a large number of UFO sighting reports. Some of these reports may be fraudulent, but most investigators have concluded that the majority are quite valid; that is, the witnesses themselves believed that they saw something real, external, artificial, and unusual. The primary aim of this book is to seek a satisfactory interpretation, or understanding, of these experiences.

On logical grounds it may be said that all possible explanations can be subdivided into two major categories, namely, A) physically real, manufactured objects that the witness could not relate to anything in his background, and B) something entirely different, such as obscure natural phenomena, hoaxes, or psychic projections. The possiblity remains, of course, that the stimulus for a report of the first type was unique to a particular witness and could prove to be quite mundane to more knowledgable and experienced people. The heart of the whole question, therefore, is whether or not there exists a subset of experiences in Category A that are unique and puzzling to mankind as a whole, including experts in every field. The majority of witnesses think so! This conviction is shared by most of the people who have diligently studied this subject. Contrary views are more popular among those who (a) feel that examination of the data would be undignified, (b) tend to reject any new concept out of hand, and (c) suspend judgment until irrefutable evidence is presented to them. Unfortunately, little progress in this perplexing field can be achieved while the mind is preoccupied with the issue of UFO existence. The reason for this dilemma is that while mentally coursing through the arguments pro and con, one's attention is deflected from discovery of more meaningful detail. The mind is then blocked from further enlightenment. Rational progress can be achieved only by setting such unwarranted skepticism aside, if only temporarily.

For the present purpose, the reader is requested to suspend his doubts and follow the argument that is developed in this book. Simply consider, for the moment, that UFOs are mechanical constructions that appear and behave in general accord with the accounts of the witnesses. Adopting this point of view cannot be harmful and may prove to be beneficial. As a working hypothesis, it will at least free the mind long enough to explore the available data. That alone is considered to be worthwhile. But its ultimate value can be assessed only upon completion of this book. At that time, we will recall that the reality of UFOs was merely assumed, as in a game, and not proven. One can then ask if this strategem led to a more thorough, comprehensive understanding of the topic. Did it unravel some of the previous mysteries and reveal their true meaning in terms of scientific facts? Did it suggest some experiments in which new ideas may be tested? Affirmative answers to these questions will establish the value of the hypothesis. On the other hand, if the hypothesis fails to bear fruit, it must be uprooted like a barren tree and thrown out of the orchard. The importance of accepting the reports at face value can hardly be overemphasized. The reader should retain this new perspective throughout the book, otherwise he may become uneasy when some detail of a sighting is brought forth and discussed uncritically. Nowhere does the author attempt to prove the validity of sighting information, or even to evaluate it. The raw data are merely accepted without bias for the purpose of exploration. It is not necessary to believe the data in order to study it. Its truth or falsity will be considered only in the final appraisal.

A fundamental precept of science is the freedom enjoyed by the theorist in devising hypotheses. While hypotheses must accommodate confirmed facts, they need not be reasonable. In fact, major advances in science have been built upon hypotheses that seem to be wildly unreasonable. Even after earning a permanent position in scientific thought, they may yet appear to be quite arbitrary and at odds with reason. In searching for new truth, one simply can not forecast the form it will take. Therefore, justifying an hypothesis is not at all necessary. As a concession to the reader, ample evidence is presented in Chapter 1 to illustrate why our hypothesis was selected. This data can be a helpful transition for the novice, but it may be skipped by the sophisticated reader who is familiar with it or who recognizes that it is logically extraneous.

The search for truth about UFOs is severely handicapped. First of all, a sighting experience cannot be reproduced in the laboratory. Neither can a UFO be captured for detailed examination. The time and location of future sightings cannot be predicted. Spontaneous sightings are so brief and widely scattered that experts and scientific instruments can not easily be brought to the scene in time to observe the action. Is further understanding, therefore, out of the question? Probably not. But this pursuit of knowledge involves a curious irony. Although the sighting reports have been derided as "anecdotal records," they are the only source of information on the subject. This reservoir must obviously be tapped if further insights are to be developed. This collection of reports undoubtedly contains some examples from Category B. Some reports that appeared to be well documented have later been exposed as pranks. Such material has occasionally been accepted uncritically, with adverse effects.—But most worldwide and issuing from diverse cultures. The common discard it. Excessive zeal in this screening process has probably deprived the investigators and the public of some valuable information. To avoid this problem and the corollary one of assessing each report, a different approach has been taken here. Reliance is placed, not so much upon the details of an individual report, as upon the correlations of many independent reports scattered world wide and issuing from diverse cultures. The common elements threading their way through a large number of reports take on the greatest meaning. Several scattered but similar reports afford the opportunity of picking up some detail from one, more from another, and so on, until a composite picture of a typical event can be drawn. The present analysis relies heavily upon these concepts, even at the risk of unwittingly including a few hoaxes, hallucinations, internal eyeflashes or whatever. The total number of reports is so large that such contamination of the source material is unlikely to distort the general findings.

The full magnitude of the UFO phenomenon is not commonly realized. A casual observer may have noted a dozen or so newspaper accounts in about as many years. He may have accidentally seen a few magazine articles sandwiched between sensational treatments of hunting polar bears and searching for treasure in the steaming Amazon. He may know of a few books on the subject, but not read them. Newspaper comments on the Condon Report (also unread) have assured him that there was nothing of special interest in the subject. It may be somewhat shocking for him to learn that the average number of reported sightings since 1947 is greater than 200 per year. Over 1,000 sightings were reported in 1967. As these figures apply only to the United States and UFOs are a global problem, the number of sighting reports is substantial. The total is not known, but there is every indication that it is on the order of 500,000 or larger.

While an individual author can do no more than scratch the surface of this voluminous collection, the results of analysis need not be proportionately compromised. After all, the portrait of a tiger can be painted from an adequate number of descriptions, although no testimony is received from the hundreds of people that have been eaten by them. To avoid bias in selecting source materials, the investigation should depend upon catalogs of sightings that have been laboriously compiled by others. As discussed in Chapter 10, the present work is considered to be only a preliminary investigation that should eventually be repeated and extended on a much more comprehensive scale. It will suffice here to demonstrate a productive method of research by unveiling some new vistas of UFOs even if, at this stage, they are seen "through a glass, darkly."

The nature of the material itself and the anticipated retracing of the steps dictate the need for extensive citing of references. Other considerations also reinforce this choice. Information throughout the book falls into several categories that should be distinguished. Yet the continual use of qualifying language for this purpose would be very burdensome and tedious. Within the framework of the hypothesis that has been adopted, we will allow ourselves to say merely that such and such *happened,* whereas it is actually known only that it was *reported.* Under the circumstances, however, the reader is entitled to know where the information came from so that he can investigate a particular incident further. Much of the information herein comes with impeccable credentials from technical and scientific sources, which can be most helpful in verifying or expanding upon points that are made. Distinctions are sometimes needed between deductions in which the author has every confidence and extrapolations or hunches that have far less secure foundations. Occasional notes can help to keep these chickens and ducks in separate coops. References and comments have been numbered serially and assembled at the end of the book so that a quick referral can usually resolve any fleeting question.

A thorough investigation of UFOs cannot be arbitrarily confined to a few technical fields in which a particular author may be trained. It becomes necessary to follow the tracks of the elusive quarry wherever they may lead. As shall be seen later, they lead into many areas of technical speciality. It can hardly be expected that an author could be uniformly competent in all of them or that his treatment of these subjects would be free of error. It can only be hoped that the general findings are valid, that the various invasions into professional provinces are not offensive to the practitioners, and that their aid will be forthcoming to correct any deficiencies.

UFOLOGY

. . . one is not entitled to a negative opinion or any opinion at all for that matter about the reality of UFOs . . . until after he has examined . . . the data
— *Stanton T. Friedman*

CHAPTER 1

CERTIFIED UFOs

Strange, disc-shaped objects started flying through the atmosphere shortly after World War II. At least that's what a lot of people said. Speculation ran rampant. Some kind of secret aircraft was being tested by the Air Force. Ours, of course. Or perhaps the Russians had made a breakthrough. Other explanations produced a long list of possibilities. People were lying for notoriety or profit. They only thought that they saw something unusual. Common things that belong in the sky were being viewed under abnormal lighting conditions. Some natural phenomenon, as yet unknown to science, was the answer. Pranksters were on the loose. Vehicles from some unknown civilization were surveying the earth.

Flying saucers, as they were called in those days, became a sensation. Newspapers, radio, and television told of new sightings. Magazine articles and books played up the idea of spacecraft from the cosmos. To many observers, the scene resembled a low-grade infection—the objects were present but unimportant. The Air Force, however, took the matter seriously and started a nationwide investigation. It was hoped that the phenomenon would prove to be a manifestation of human silliness and fade

1

away. It did not. A quarter of a century passed and the situation did not change much. True, the Air Force finally tired of its mission and abandoned the chase. But the UFOs are still with us.

The possibility that the witnesses may have been telling the truth is strongly suspected when a general uniformity of the reports is noticed. For example, one may be impressed that the same type of object was reported by, say, a French physician in 1954 and a Brazilian peasant in 1968. It is especially significant in such cases when a particularly bizarre detail is mentioned by both witnesses. One might suspect collusion, but this is usually extremely unlikely or completely impossible. As in this example, the Brazilian peasant may have been deprived of all communication beyond his own village and never heard of UFOs. It would have to be considered remarkable if his report echoed the content of another one from a distant land. Is there any way in which the trustworthiness of such reports can be established?

Reliability of Reports

The theoretical question of reliability became quite important during the years when intercontinental ballistic missiles were being developed. These weapons, implanted in underground silos in the western states, must remain on stand-by for long periods but they must always be operable. They are extremely complex mechanisms; consequently, many things can go wrong with them. The strategic posture of the United States is defined by the existence of these missiles plus the assurance that they would work if called upon. Every aspect of these weapons, from their control systems to their maintenance schedules, had to be planned to meet the stringent demands of reliability. This obligation fostered a new and powerful tool that is known as Reliability Theory.[1] This theory establishes the relationship between the performance of a complex system and its subsystems and components. If the reliability of the individual components is known, the theory may be employed to compute the reliability of the complete system. Conversely, if the required reliability of the overall system is specified, the theory can be used to establish the requisite reliability of all the constituents. In the latter case, each element that goes into the system must be tested extensively to prove that it meets the prescribed standards. The mathematical statement of reliability is a single number from 0 to 1.0, similar to the scale of probability. Absolute reliability, represented by 1.0, is theoretically unattainable.

This theory has been successfully applied to UFO reports. As with any complex system, the problem was first broken down into its finest elements. Such factors as the number of witnesses, their training in aerial observation, and the circumstances of the sighting were isolated. Details of the original documentation were accounted for with emphasis upon interviews of the witnesses and the professional qualifications of the interviewers. Finally, the quality of secondary reports that had been prepared from the original documents was assessed. Reliability Theory was then used to derive an equation expressing the reliability of a report. One hundred sixty (160) sightings from Japan, France, Venezuela, and the U.S.A. were selected and analysed.[2]

In 1961, a large, spherical object was observed by a famous television commentator and hundreds of other people. It hovered over the city of Indianapolis, Indiana, at two different altitudes before moving away rapidly to the south. It was apparently metallic with a steady green light on top and flashing red lights on the bottom. Just above its equator was a row of windows. The Reliability Index for this sighting turned out to be in excess of 0.999! In other words, one can be well assured that this incident took place according to the reports, although absolute certainty is ruled out. Even the structural details of UFOs, such as the windows in this instance, must be taken seriously when they are included in highly reliable reports.

Other interesting sightings whose Reliability Indices were also found to be greater than 0.999 are summarized below:

a. Bright light on shadowy object. Confirmed by radar. Scrambled jet fighter had radar lock-on. UFO broke into three pieces that all flew away.

b. Rigid submarine-shaped cloud with metallic disc spiraling around it. Disc flew over a four mile area then returned to the "submarine."

c. Bright, cigar-shaped object with windows. Hovered then left rapidly. Emitted strong strands or fibers that evaporated upon touch and stained hands.

d. Ovoid, aluminum-colored object. Landed on a hill. Grass flattened in rough circle 60 ft in diameter. Moved as a white cloud with fuzzy edges.

e. Two convex, disc-shaped objects near a large balloon. Speed changes and extremely fast departure. Size estimated between 200 and 300 ft.

f. Night lights in rigid pattern. Approached, hovered, then flew away. Inferred size about 150 ft. No structure discernible but impression of metallic surface. Car could not catch it upon departure.

g. Bright glowing object proceeding over hills in undulatory path.

These examples are especially important because they are quite typical UFO reports. It would be difficult to dismiss these events or to interpret them in any way other than at face value.

One word of caution: A report is not proven to be fraudulent even though it may warrant a low Reliability Index. A single witness who is neither technically trained nor professionally involved in aerial observations would rank low on the reliability scale. Yet a sharp-eyed farmer from Pennsylvania would be perfectly capable of reporting a sighting with sincerity and accuracy. Consequently, all reports should be studied without prejudice, unless of course, a hoax or misinterpretation has been proven in a particular instance. Only on this basis can the maximum amount of information be brought to bear upon the perplexing problem of UFOs.

Air Force Experience

The involvement of the U.S. Air Force in the UFO phenomenon is practically synonymous with the modern history of UFOs. It is a long and intricate story. As previous authors have handled that subject expertly, it will be omitted here.[3] Let it suffice to recall that Air Force investigations were handled by an office at Wright-Patterson Air Force Base in Ohio under various code names, the latest and longest-lived being Project Blue Book. The period of active investigation began in the summer of 1947 and continued until December 1969, at which time the Air Force disbanded the investigative team and stored its UFO files.[4]

The general impression left by this activity was that all UFOs had been explained in terms of familiar things. But hardly anything could be further from the truth. According to Captain Edward J. Ruppelt, former head of Project Blue Book, a panel of distinguished scientists was convened in 1953 to consider, among other possibilities, if UFOs were interplanetary space craft.[5] By that time, an analysis of 1,593 sightings had been prepared for their examination. Considerable effort had been expended in attempts to determine what familiar entity might have stimulated each report. Many reports were definitely established as having been confused observations of airplanes, balloons, astronomical bodies, etc. Yet there remained 26.94%, or 429 cases, that were "Unknowns." If the stimulus for an observation could have reasonably been an airplane, the case was tagged as "Probable" airplane. If it were remotely possible that the witness could have been viewing an airplane, the case was tagged "Possible" airplane. Other interesting pigeon holes for parking hoary sightings were labeled "Psychological" and "Insufficient Data." The appellation "Unknown" did not mean that the object of the report had merely not been identified. Rather, it represented a definite conclusion that the object *was* unknown. While the above 429 cases were admitted to be unidentified, the actual number was very likely much greater. For example, airplanes were alleged to be the explanation of 11.76% of the sightings. Yet most of the cases in that category were not confirmed as airplanes, and were assigned the subcategories of "Probable" and "Possible" airplanes. By adding all the cases in every category in which identity was definitely established, one finds that only 11.21%, or 179 cases, were actually identified. In other words, 88.79% were not identified. The situation was evidently worse than that, because in Ruppelt's own words, "About 4,400 had actually been received." Most of these were rejected before the Air Force percentages were calculated. Considering that only 179 cases out of the original 4,400 were conclusively identified, it is obvious that only about 4% of the reports were explained. The remainder were not explained. But even accepting the Air Force figure of 179 "Unknowns" gives a clear message: they had plenty of UFOs.

Published data for subsequent years indicate that Blue Book handled several hundred reports each year, running from a low of 378 in 1959 to a high of 982 in 1957.[6] Their performance seemed to improve as the percentages of "Unknowns" fell from around 8-to-10% in the early period down to about 2% in 1965. There were obviously so many arbitrary aspects to this numbers game that little meaningful information can be extracted from the tabulated results. It is clear, however, that the Air Force had its hands full of UFOs and officially said so.

Residue in Colorado

In the fall of 1966, an independent study of UFOs was undertaken by a staff of scientists at the University of Colorado under the direction of Dr. Edward U. Condon. This distinguished physicist had previously served the U.S. as head of the National Bureau of Standards and had been elected by his peers to the presidency of both the American Physical Society and the American Association for the Advancement of Science. Initial funding of about $260,000 for the project was eventually extended to over half a million dollars. Results of the study were published in a tome with more than its share of heavy, technical jargon. Certainly more people have scanned newspaper summaries of its findings than have studied the full report. Several hundred UFO sightings were considered by the scientists, but attention was focused upon 59 individual examples for in-depth analysis. One of the more widely circulated quotations from Condon was the general conclusion that "nothing has come from the study of UFOs in the past 21 years that has added to scientific knowledge."[7] He further elaborated "that further extensive study of UFOs probably cannot be justified in the expectation that science will be advanced thereby." These appraisals were largely responsible for the sharp decline in interest in UFOs, the reluctance on the part of news media to publish subsequent sightings, and the folding of Project Blue Book. An overwhelming mass of technical detail was assembled in the report. Much of it is most helpful in the study of UFOs, but some curious aspects are found in the case studies.

In analyzing a famous sighting that occurred in McMinnville, Oregon, and the photographs taken by the witnesses, all the factors that were considered appeared "to be consistent with the assertion that an extraordinary flying object, silvery, metallic, disc-shaped, tens of meters in diameter, and evidently artificial, flew within sight of two witnesses."[8] That sounds very similar to an ordinary UFO.

In another instance, a white, rapidly moving object was observed visually and confirmed simultaneously by air traffic control radars at two Air Force bases. A scrambled jet fighter, vectored to the object, reported a radar lock-on. The UFO circled behind the jet and stuck with it through evasive maneuvers. The Condon report devoted eight pages to evaluating this incident and concluded that ". . . the probability that at least one genuine UFO was involved appears to be fairly high."[9] How interesting!

On still another occasion, one of three lights maneuvering over a school flew silently toward three women and an 11-year-old girl and stopped overhead at an altitude between 20 and 30 ft. It was described as a solid disc about the size of a car. That an unusual object was flying over the school was verified by two policemen who had responded to a telephone call. Most of this sighting was ascribed to the planet Jupiter except that the conclusion stated "No explanation is attempted to account for the close UFO encounter reported by three women and a young girl."[10] How quaint!

Actually, no more than 25% of the cases studied by the Condon team were successfully identified. Here is another official pronouncement that indicates the existence of unknowns in stark contrast to the general impression that there are no such things. It should be observed that this study did not undertake a systematic examination of the many thousands of cases on record at Project Blue Book, nor the approximately 700 cases that had been at that time officially designated as "Unknowns."

Civilian Groups

Probably the most effective work in the UFO field has been conducted by unofficial, civilian organizations. Most notable among these are the National Investigations Committee on Aerial Phenomena of Washington, D.C., founded by Major Donald Keyhoe, and the Aerial Phenomena Research Organization of Tucson, Arizona, founded by Coral and Jim Lorenzen. The number of cases of unexplained observations is enormous, and many of them have been well researched. It is estimated that the files of these organizations amount to 15,000 and 10,000 cases, respectively, with very limited overlap or duplication. Although publications issued by these organizations were reviewed during the Colorado study, these reservoirs of information on UFOs were not consulted.

Scientific Analysis

One of the most prominent and respected individuals of long term association with UFOs is Dr. J. Allen Hynek. Dr. Hynek is a noted astronomer at Northwestern University and is in charge of the Dearborn Observatory. He is best known to the public through his role as a civilian consultant to the Air Force during its investigations of UFOs. It is most instructive to trace the evolution of his views. He was initially called upon to examine reports received by the Air Force to determine which ones might be instances of astronomical objects causing UFO reports. Apparently quite a few people thought that Venus, other planets, or astronomical objects were UFOs. Of the first 237 reports received by the Air Force and analysed by Hynek, approximately one-third appeared to be of astronomical origin.[11] The remaining two-thirds, apparently not associated with astronomical displays, were about equally divided between those for which some reasonable explanation was suggested by the nature of the report and those for which no explanation was evident. At that time, Hynek had a low opinion for the concept of UFOs and "regarded the whole subject as rank nonsense, the product of silly seasons, and a peculiarly American craze that would run its course as all popular crazes do."[12] During the middle years of his association with the Air Force, however, he became troubled by a hard core of reports that continued to defy explanations in common terms. In a magazine article he listed outer space as a possible source of the unidentified objects and called for serious, scientific study of UFOs.[13] In an open letter to his scientific colleagues he "strongly urged the Air Force to ask physical and social scientists of stature to make a respectable, scholarly study of the UFO phenomenon."[14] He went on to say that he could not shrug off the UFO problem because the unexplained cases contained "frequent allusions to recurrent kinematic, geometric, and luminescent characteristics," a point that will take on extraordinary significance in later chapters. Before the Committee of Science and Astronautics of the U.S. House of Representatives he pressed his suggestion ". . . that there is scientific pay dirt in the UFO phenomenon—possibly extremely valuable pay dirt—and that therefore a scientific effort on a much larger scale than any heretofore should be mounted for a frontal attack on this problem."[15] The following year, a similar appeal for action was issued at a session devoted to UFOs at the annual meeting of the

American Association for the Advancement of Science.[16]

Eventually, Dr. Hynek published the findings of his own scientific analysis of UFOs.[17] As a point of conservatism, he rejected any report submitted by a single witness and studied selected multi-witness cases in which he had been personally involved. His conclusions should be convincing to the most skeptical reader. He finds that disc-shaped, metallic craft of unknown origin are flying around during the daytime. At night, their presence is indicated by peculiar lights moving in typically jerky patterns. From sightings at close range he discloses a) some structural details of the craft, b) physical evidence that they have left on the ground, and c) human-like creatures occupying the craft. To say the least, this book should be on every must-read list.

Springboard to Discovery

Some UFO reports have been found to be extremely reliable by methods that are technically sound and employed extensively in other fields. The Air Force, in effect, has been telling the public for many years that UFOs have been flying around in great numbers. This point was confirmed by an expensive, independent study conducted by scientists at the University of Colorado. Civilian groups have been collecting and investigating UFO reports by the tens of thousands and have written highly reputable books about them. A leading astronomer who has been professionally associated with the subject for 25 years found that his original attitude of scoffing at UFOs was gradually replaced by the conclusion, established by scientific means, that UFOs are real. It would seem that these factors lend a reasonable basis for adopting the reality of UFOs as a tentative perspective. If they are some strange kind of craft, a considerable amount of detail about them might be discovered by careful attention to what the witnesses have said.

. . . the scientific world at large is in for a shock when it becomes aware of the astonishing nature of the UFO phenomenon and its bewildering complexity.

— James E. McDonald

CHAPTER 2

THE VEHICLES

The belief that people are poor observers is widely held; they are easily mistaken about what they have seen, or they fail to notice details correctly. Experiments by psychologists, on the contrary, have shown that the inherent ability of people to absorb visual information is very great. Subjects in one experiment were shown 600 different pictures in rapid succession. Shortly thereafter they were able to identify new ones that had been added to the collection, with an average accuracy over 98%. Their score fell to only 92% when the test was delayed for one week. Not only is the power of visual recognition evidently quite strong for most people, their retention is also good, at least for short periods. In discussing UFO sightings before a Congressional Committee, a noted psychologist explained that, even in unexpected and stressful situations, ". . . the average witness often retains an accurate, almost photographic record of the event."[1] A person's recollection of an event can be recovered in considerable detail on the basis of recognition. The victim of a criminal attack, for example, may recognize his assailant in a line-up although he may be unable to describe him accurately. Similarly, the use of graded sketches of eyes, noses, and mouths permits a witness, with the help of a police artist, to develop a satisfactory portrait of a suspect that could not be done solely from a description. People simply are limited in their ability to describe what they have seen or to communicate an experience. Because advanced psychological techniques involving recognition have seldom been employed in eliciting information from UFO witnesses, the available data is handicapped by being almost exclusively descriptive in nature. This fact has undoubtedly frustrated progress in this field.

Discs

Nine large discs flying near Mt. Rainier, Washington, set off the modern hubbub about UFOs. They were sighted by businessman Kenneth Arnold from his own plane in June 1947. He estimated that they were 100 ft in diameter and traveling at least 1,200 miles per hour.[2] These objects resembled pie plates, but newspaper accounts of "flying saucers" introduced a new expression into English. The term eventually became obsolete, however, as people began reporting objects with shapes very unlike saucers: the more generic term "unidentified flying objects" became more suitable.

Even a cursory examination of a file of sighting reports will impress the researcher that most of the objects appeared to be discs. Seldom will the descriptions be entirely clear, and some will admit alternative interpretations. An object described merely as "round" may have been a disc, but it may also have been a sphere, or a cylinder viewed from one end. An object may have appeared "oval shaped," while in reality it was only a disc that was tipped slightly off the line of vision. It is not always easy to establish the exact shape of the reported objects, nor even to select several categories of shapes that are mutually exclusive and free from ambiguity. At any rate, the disc-shaped UFO with a diameter about 10 times its thickness is almost universally accepted as standard. This point was raised in an Air Force report[3] as early as 1949, and it has been verified by several statistical studies. Because various and non-compatible categories were selected in the independent studies, results cannot be directly compared. However, the National Investigations Committee on Aerial Phenomena found that the discs in Air Force cases through 1963 ranged from 26% to 56%, depending upon several reasonable assumptions regarding the ambiguities just mentioned.[4] The author independently analyzed 447 short-range sightings that occurred in the decade from November 23, 1958, through November 22, 1968. These sightings should have provided the witnesses excellent opportunities to observe the shapes. In 77 instances in which the shapes were noted, roughly 50% of the objects appeared to be discs.[5] A similar result may be calculated from still another study, although it is extremely difficult to determine which of the 33 categories used in it should be taken as discs.[6]

The most important contribution of this last investigation is an organized disclosure of different types of UFOs within the general category of discs. One must be cautious here, for while the primary common feature is axial symmetry in the vertical direction, some of the shapes could easily be labeled something other than "disc." The researcher obtained 150 photographs of UFOs from which were culled those showing mere blobs of light devoid of any details. He then made sketches of the remaining 63 objects at the same scale, and suppressing all backgrounds, assembled the images in a single diagram. Rather than displaying a general uniformity or a clustering of a few types as would be expected, these sketches show a wide diversity of appearances.

One object had been photographed at different angles by the same witness. In a few other instances, the same type of UFO had apparently been photographed by different people at different places and times. Of special interest in this regard is a photograph taken at McMinnville, Oregon, in June 1950 that stumped the Condon staff. An almost identical object was photographed by a French military pilot near Rouen, France, in March 1954. Another pair of photographs also seem to depict the same type of object that is easily distinguishable from the McMinnville-Rouen pair. One of these pictures was taken near Rio de Janeiro in May,

1952, while the other was taken from a fighter plane in Argentina about 2 years later.

Also included in the 63 diagrams were 7 instances in which hoaxes were suspected or had been proved. Setting these cases aside, along with the duplications above, still leaves a total of about 50 different UFO models in this general category. Variations of shape in this category that appear to be most common are:

a) Discs having one or both sides that are convex, thus resembling either a discus or a lens, and
b) Discs with a dome on the top sometimes giving the appearance of a hat or a World War I helmet.

Fuselages

A famous sighting that was carried by Project Blue Book as an "unknown" took place early one morning in the spring of 1966. While driving near Temple, Oklahoma, a man had to stop his car because a large object was blocking the highway. Its shape reminded him of the fuselage of a Douglas C-124 Globemaster. He could detect no appendages, such as wings, engines, or tail, although there was a transparent blister on the top. Its surface was very smooth. As the witness approached, the object rose into the air and departed at high speed.[7] During the summer of 1973, a similar object was observed from a distance of a city block as it hovered and maneuvered over Macon, Georgia. Five people described it as a "long tube" like a cigar, being larger than a light plane but smaller than a Boeing 727.[8] According to the previous statistical studies, these elongated UFOs apparently account for about 10% of all sightings. They have been aptly compared to airplane bodies as more explicit descriptions have indicated that they are rather blunt on one end but somewhat tapered on the other.

Spheres

Throughout the spring of 1973, hundreds of sightings were reported in southern Missouri. Notices of this activity were carried in specialty periodicals, but few, if any, metropolitan newspapers commented on it.[9] Several teams of investigators converged upon the area, including the principals of the International UFO Bureau. These investigators, during a total of 11 days of research over a period of several weeks, located 200 people who had seen a UFO and tape recorded interviews with them. They, themselves, also experienced two sightings. On one occasion, the relative size of the object was compared to a pea held at arms length, giving ample opportunity to observe its shape, to discern some structural details, and to estimate its size. It was a sphere about 15 ft in diameter.[10]

Near the end of the war in Vietnam a spherical object with a luminous, orange glow was sighted at high altitude over Hanoi where it remained nearly stationary for about an hour and a half. Thinking that some kind of air raid was imminent, the North Vietnamese fired three anti-aircraft missiles at it. They were completely ineffective, however, as none could reach the extreme altitude of the spherical UFO.[11]

These two examples will illustrate the dozens of reports of this relatively common type. They seem to be most often perfectly spherical but some variations occur, as follows:

a) Flattened spheres or spheroids, and
b) Spheres with a flange around the equator like the rings of Saturn.

Potpourri

Witnesses have used a wide assortment of words and comparisons in describing UFOs. While some of them may be synonyms for the major types discussed above, it appears that many are not. Because some of the more odd-ball expressions have been used several times in widely scattered sightings, the descriptions are more likely to be valid than mere bumbling attempts at communication. Typical, but rarely occurring, examples are:

football	water tank
dumbbell	plates rim-to-rim

oval	mushroom
egg	toy top
diamond	parachute
cone	cushion
hamburger sandwich	lampshade

Assuming that a few of these allusions are moderately accurate leads to a proliferation of UFO models that begins to stretch the imagination. But that discomfort is an inadequate basis for discounting the record. A native boy, suddenly transported from the familiar bush of his homeland to a freeway in Los Angeles, would be amazed at the diversity of vehicles passing by. He might quickly realize that part of the reason was related to their different purposes. He could see that the size of the load was important, pickup trucks and huge trailer rigs being used to haul different amounts of freight. Similarly for the number of passengers carried by sports cars versus buses. Much less obvious to him would be the very important influence of competition among the manufacturers and personal preference of the buyers concerning economy, image, and convenience. This little allegory cannot explain the multiplicity of UFO types. It should serve, however, to prevent a setback in an investigation proven to be uncomfortably complex.

It is known, at least, that highly specialized vehicles may display weird configurations. Consider the Lunar Excursion Module. It is designed exclusively to lower two men gently onto the surface of the moon and lift them back into lunar orbit for a rendevous with a companion vehicle. Major determinants of its design are the need to fly in a vacuum and a gravitational field that is only one-sixth that on earth. By its ungainly aspect it mimics a giant insect much better than a proper spacecraft.

Size

Another old bugbear has plagued the study of UFOs: theoretically, the size of an unknown object flying through the sky at a considerable distance cannot be judged at all. A relatively small object at short range may subtend the same angle at the observer's eye as a larger object farther away. Without some additional point of reference, therefore, the estimated size of a UFO is of little value. But the circumstances of many sightings provide the necessary clues. Very great distance is suggested when an object is obscured by atmospheric haze in comparison to another whose distance is known. Also, the relationship of a UFO to its surroundings often helps. A UFO may be seen rising from behind a row of trees, passing in front of a mountain range, hovering under a cloud bank, or fleeing from a military jet. For limited ranges, the depth perception afforded by having two eyes provides a subjective measure of the distance. Disturbances on the ground directly under a UFO may be located. At low altitude, the width of a UFO can be readily assessed if it is seen to block a two-lane highway. Marks left on the ground by a landed UFO are a very reliable basis for judging its size. As these reference points have been involved in thousands of sightings, the data on UFO sizes is far from meaningless, especially when they are derived from close-hand observations.

One would expect the conventional methods of statistics to be most helpful in analyzing the size data. By separating cases involving only discs, for example, one should discover estimated sizes clustering about the actual dimensions of several different models. But that has not been the author's experience. The data simply display no such tendency. Contamination of the sample is suspected to be the cause of this difficulty, namely, unwitting inclusion of various types of UFOs within a particular classification. In addition, people are known to be rather poor at estimating dimensions.

The diameters of discs, nevertheless, have been estimated to cover the enormous range from about 2 ft to 300 ft. Familiar objects with corresponding dimensions would be a large serving tray and a football field. But let there be no mistake here, several different models of UFOs are involved and this disparity has nothing to do with human error. Other shapes have also been estimated at various sizes:

Shape	Dimension	Range of Sizes (feet)
Cylinder	length	12 to 210
Egg	length	9 to 75
Sphere	diameter	6 to 21

Perhaps this situation would come into sharper focus with a large-scale analysis of the data using a computer. For the present, one can only depend upon the most reliable estimates made at close range and a general acquaintance with the literature. References are regrettably omitted here because of the prodigious scale of the data-retrieval problem. The primary UFO types appear to be:

PROBES: Spheres and discs between 1- and 3-ft diameter that are almost certainly sensing devices, either preprogramed or remotely controlled. They have been seen to emerge from standard craft, fly around for extended periods, then return for pickup. The kind of measurements that they take can only be guessed.

SMALL: Three principal types eventually belong to this group;

a)   An egg-shaped machine about 6- to 8-ft long that flies with the long axis vertical, comparable in size to a compact sedan.

b)   An elongated cylinder without external appendages that flies in the direction of its axis, comparable in size to the body of a jet fighter.

c)   A spherical object about 15 ft in diameter.

STANDARD: This group, accounting for about half the sightings is dominated by the basic disc with numerous

LARGE:

> variations. Most common size is about 25- to 35-ft diameter.

LARGE: Several different types. Most frequently reported is a disc about 100 ft diameter. An even larger one, several stories tall inside, probably has a diameter between 250- and 300-ft. A large cigar-shaped craft should also be included here.

CARRIER: Seen only at very high altitude is a gigantic, cigar-shaped machine that is probably twice as large as an aircraft carrier and, perhaps, as much as 1 mile in length. Smaller craft have been seen to be discharged from them in large numbers.

Structural Details

Usually, the exterior surface of UFOs is reported to be extremely smooth. Many witnesses have commented upon this aspect, expressing surprise that they were unable to detect any line of adjoining plates on the surface or any rivets. In a few instances, a door has been seen to open in the side where the witness could not detect an outline before it started to move. Also, upon closing, the line demarking the door opening could no longer be discerned, although the witness was only a few feet away.[12] This characteristic of the surface may be related to electrical conduction in the skin as explored in a later chapter.

The exterior surface is not normally broken by any kind of structural feature although openings have been observed in great numbers. In a study of 50 such cases, openings were shown to be usually round or rectangular but sometimes of irregular shape. Their arrangement occurred in different patterns on different types of UFOs.[13] These windows seem to be most common on the fuselage-shaped vehicles, usually being dispersed in a single row of 4 or 5 along the side. The number, shape, and location of windows seems to vary considerably on other types. A thorough study of this detail should help to delineate specific UFO models, but again, this task would be too cumbersome without a computer.

A most interesting feature on some models is an elevator that is lowered while the UFO remains hovering several feet above the ground. This detail is so unique that it alone may isolate a particular type. These vehicles have evidently visited West Virginia (1965), Minnesota (1967), and Nebraska (1967).[14] It is quite possible that a careful plot of similar sightings in which all factors were compatible would reconstruct the itinerary of an individual craft.

The literature is full of accounts of other structural elements such as landing gear, stairways, balustrades, and antennas. More than once, people have looked in the windows of landed vehicles to discover chairs, benches, tables, lights, and control consoles. Others have gone inside. This very important area should receive much more attention than it has in the past.

> . . . A scientist, by definition, is
> concerned with an objective
> evaluation of data; he applies
> proper figures and cites correct
> facts; he is unbiased as far as
> humanly possible, in drawing
> his conclusions; his dedication
> is to progress in the search for
> truth.
>
> — Immanuel Velikovsky

CHAPTER 3

COMPOSITION AND LUMINOSITY

Quite apart from the general appearances of UFOs as established
by their sizes, shapes, and structural details, they also seem to be
very colorful. From a compilation of 923 instances of close
encounters with UFOs, approximately half of the witnesses had
something to say about the color.[1] As these descriptions vary in
the extreme, a satisfactory mental image of a UFO can not be
readily conceived. What sense can be made of such diverse and
conflicting expressions as "silvery," "luminous," "brilliant
blue," "glowing orange,"and "blinding"? But this bewildering
melange will yield some surprising and valuable insights into the
UFO phenomenon when it is examined carefully. All such
descriptions certainly can not apply at the same time, hence, it
must be understood that UFOs take on a variety of colors under
different circumstances.

Descriptive terms used by the witnesses in referring to colors
tend to fall into five, distinct categories that can be labeled as
Metallic, Soft Glow, Spectral Colors, Bright White, and Multi-
colored. Typical expressions of the witnesses that illustrate the
first four categories are tabulated below.

Metallic	Soft Glow	Spectral Colors	Bright White
aluminum	glowing white	orange	burning magnesium
silvery	luminous	red	very dazzling
metallic	fluorescent	orange-red	intense bright
chrome		fiery red	brilliant
shiny		bluish	bright
reflective		yellow	intensely luminous
gray		bluish-green	blinding white

When more than one color was reported, the witnesses usually indicated whether the colors appeared at the same time or serially, that is, one after another. Therefore, the fifth category naturally divides into two subcategories, Simultaneous and Sequential. From the 477 most recent UFO encounters in the compilation by Vallee, all references to multi-colors are shown below along with the identifying case numbers.

Multi-Colored

Simultaneous		Sequential	
blue, green, and orange flashes	540	orange to fluorescent green	670
multi-colored	572	varied from white to red	692
yellow-orange with blue-green edges	657	reddish-orange to blinding white	741
very bright with dark underside	736	white to yellow to blue to green	782
blue, red, and green bands	796	white to greenish-blue	821
red to orange to white together with blue underside 838			

The last example appears to be a combination of color changes occurring at the same time that the underside remained blue. Having detected a logical pattern in the colors ascribed to UFOs, one should next examine the various categories individually in considerable detail.

Metallic Surface

Fifty-two witnesses attempted to describe a metallic surface as follows:

Number	Using These Terms	Alluding To
13	Silver, silvery	Silver
6	Aluminum, aluminum-like	Aluminum
12	Metallic	Unspecified
13	Chrome, shiny, reflective	Polished
12	Gray metallic, dark gray	Dull
56*		

*The total does not add up to fifty-two because compound expressions were tabulated twice.

The witnesses were clearly describing the polished surface of a "white" metal except, perhaps, the twelve who related an impression of dull gray. Eleven of these latter observations, however, occurred under adverse lighting conditions during twilight or at night. Under an overcast sky or through atmospheric haze, a jet airliner that is known to be bright aluminum takes on the appearance of dull gray or even dark gray on the lower half. Therefore, these reports are clearly compatible with the others and there seems to be little doubt about a metallic appearance of UFOs.

Most people encounter only a few white metals in their daily experience, such as aluminum cookware, chrome-plated automobile parts, and stainless steel kitchen utensils. Naturally any white metal would usually be described by reference to these familiar objects. Because quite a few unfamiliar metals are also white, the homey descriptions by witnesses cannot be taken literally. Some hints as to the actual metal of UFOs might be inferred from the properties required by their flight characteristics and mode of propulsion. In view of a need for strength, lightness, and resistance to heat, titanium would be a good candidate. Also, magnesium. Some fragments of a UFO that exploded in South America were subjected to extensive analysis and found to consist of extremely pure magnesium.[2] Some of these samples were later analysed at the University of Colorado. A high content of strontium was unexpectedly found although strontium is not known to be added to commercial magnesium. Despite this interesting result, the crystal structure suggested that the sample was unlikely to have been part of a manufactured article. It was concluded that it did not have an "unearthly composition" and the reader is left with the implication that it could not have been part of a UFO.[3] A dissenting view that was issued independently, however, judged the metallurgy of the magnesium to be quite unique.[4]

On the whole, science should be considered as an open-ended inquiry, that is, one in which progress and understanding tend to continue indefinitely. Thus, a reliable theory that has served well for decades may be upset by a new discovery. It must then be abandoned in favor of a new concept that is a closer and more comprehensive approximation of nature. Such notions grow to maturity as they elucidate some field of science and prove their resilience in the face of continued progress. One such area that may be considered as a cornerstone of science is the internal structure of atoms and the Periodic Table of the Elements.[5] While this theory is still subject to future revision and refinement, there are no major gaps in the scientific understanding of the natural elements. They are the raw materials from which any object must be fabricated on earth. As the same elements have been measured throughout the universe by analysis of starlight, they are also the raw materials from which an object must be fabricated anywhere. Of this one may be nearly certain, that the metal of a spaceship visiting earth will be composed exclusively of elements that are already known. To be sure, technological superiority may be evidenced by unusual purity or new mixtures and crystal structures, but not necessarily. Modern science is perfectly adequate to support spaceflight by man, hence, advances in metallurgy beyond current knowledge are not required to bring visitors to the earth. In other words, an unearthly composition of UFO fragments should not be expected.

While windows and transparent cupolas on top of disc-shaped UFOs are frequently mentioned, on two occasions in the sample witnesses thought that the entire object was transparent. In one of these, a disc-shaped object flew above a bicyclist for 5 kilometers at a height of 6 meters. It "was luminous and seemed made of glass."[6] In the other instance, witnesses in a stalled vehicle saw occupants inside a "brilliant, transparent, mushroomshaped object."[7] These reports are too rare to justify a separate category. of UFOs but they should be kept in mind as possible clues to an advanced material technology, that is, a state of metal that transmits light.

Soft Glow

The metallic appearance of UFOs in the previous category is a result of light reflecting off their polished surfaces. But witnesses frequently indicate that the UFO itself was luminous. As distinguished from a wide variety of white or colored lights that are reportedly attached to UFOs, light is observed radiating from the entire object or its immediate vicinity. Occasional references to "sparks" immediately suggest that some kind of electrical phenomenon is involved.

An electrical discharge of sufficient strength in the air surrounding a UFO would produce a soft, white glow, known as corona. Such discharge can sometimes be seen at night along a high-voltage transmission line but they are not visible in the daylight. Coronas could be responsible for the typical distinction between metallic discs that are so commonly reported in the daytime and diffuse lights most often seen at night. They would adhere to the UFO surface and gradually dissipate a short distance away, thereby appearing as the "halo" often described by witnesses. Unfortunately, an ordinary corona is not likely to be the correct explanation for the white glow.

The designer of a high-voltage transmission line would seek to use the smallest possible cable to minimize the amount of copper required, the weight suspended between towers, and the number of towers per mile of line. He would select electrical potentials as high as 750,000 volts to reduce the power losses from internal heating of the cable. High voltage, however, would induce power losses through corona discharge unless offset by the use of larger cable sizes. As electrical lines of force converge toward the center of a cable, electrical field strengths at its surface will be smaller for cables of greater diameter. A well-designed transmission line will therefore balance these and other considerations for a minimum construction cost and utilize a cable just large enough to prevent corona under normal operating conditions. Under occasional atmospheric conditions favoring electrical breakdown, corona will occur at field strengths on the order of 3,000,000 volts per meter.[8] The possibility of such extreme electrical fields being developed near a large object, such as a UFO having gently curving surfaces, seems quite remote.

Even so, some technical implications arise in the context of white glow. As some sort of electrical phenomenon is suspected, it can be postulated that a UFO has:

a) a large, negative potential relative to ground that causes electrons to leak into the atmosphere,
b) an alternating potential that agitates gas atoms in its vicinity, or
c) an alternating current within its skin acting as an antenna to radiate energy into the atmosphere.

The following discussions will greatly clarify this aspect of UFO luminosity.

Rainbow Colors

Nearly every color of the rainbow has been ascribed to UFOs. Typical statements by witnesses include most shades of the color spectrum from blue-violet through green, yellow, and orange, to red. Descriptive language of witnesses in the sample cases under study are tabulated in the following chart in accordance with their appropriate positions in the spectrum. Where mixtures of pure colors are implied, the components are inserted in their color zones and connected by vertical lines, such as for "purple" being composed of blue and red.

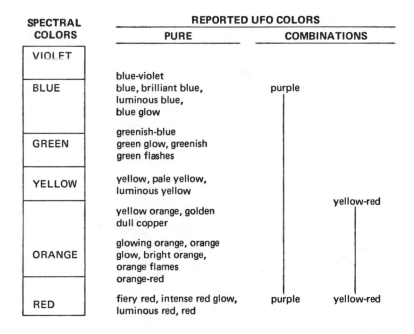

SPECTRAL COLORS	REPORTED UFO COLORS	
	PURE	COMBINATIONS
VIOLET		
BLUE	blue-violet blue, brilliant blue, luminous blue, blue glow	purple
GREEN	greenish-blue green glow, greenish green flashes	
YELLOW	yellow, pale yellow, luminous yellow	
	yellow orange, golden dull copper	yellow-red
ORANGE	glowing orange, orange glow, bright orange, orange flames orange-red	
RED	fiery red, intense red glow, luminous red, red	purple yellow-red

Before probing for an interpretation of these statements, a digression is required to review the origin and nature of light. Light is produced within atoms of matter. When atoms become sufficiently agitated by collision among themselves or with other elementary particles or by absorption of electromagnetic radiation, one or more electrons are elevated out of their normal energy states (orbits) or removed from the atom completely. As electrons fall back into these vacancies, a certain amount of energy is released. It is radiated away as a photon having that specific energy and a corresponding wave length. X-rays are usually produced from such transitions in the deeper layers of atoms. But radiation in the ultraviolet, visible, and infrared regions of the spectrum are emitted by transitions involving the more loosely bound, outer electrons, that is, those responsible for the chemical behavior of the atom. Within the visible region, a stream of photons having the same wavelength (also frequency) will be perceived as a unique, pure, spectral color ranging from violet to red, with the shorter wavelengths toward the violet end.

The amount of energy involved in these electronic transitions is well known for all the elements in the science of atomic structure and spectroscopy. Therefore, the element responsible for emission of photons of a particular energy and color can be identified in laboratory tests.[9] This knowledge has been put to extremely valuable service in the spectrographic analysis of chemical samples and in identifying the atoms responsible for the emission of light in stars. It may also prove to be advantageous here.

Very common descriptions such as "surrounded with a red glow"[10] and "wrapped in a blue haze"[11] clearly indicate that the source of UFO luminosity is not the object itself but the proximate air. One wonders, therefore, if the specific atoms in the air responsible for the light can be identified. Of course, it would be necessary to know what gases are present in the atmosphere but that is common knowledge. The accompanying table gives the number of cubic feet of each constituent gas in 1,000,000 cubic feet of air.[12] Hydrocarbons are also present in variable amounts depending upon local conditions but these pollutants are disregarded. As most UFO sightings are in remote areas such as mountains, deserts, and farmlands where air is relatively clean, it is assumed that the hydrocarbons are insignificant as a source of light.

Also shown in the table is the number of spectral lines in the visible region that is emitted by each species. With a total of several hundred lines involved, it could become quite troublesome to associate one particular color emitted by a UFO with one specific gas. However, several factors tend to simplify the task. If a large number of the tabulated spectral lines were emitted simultaneously, their mixture would produce white light instead of the individual, pure colors that were reported for UFOs in this category. Furthermore, spectral lines from a given atom are not

Gases	Volume (ft^3)	Approximate Number of Visible Spectral Lines
Nitrogen	780,840	79
Oxygen	209,406	79
Argon	9,340	219
Carbon Dioxide	300	7
Neon	18.18	153
Helium	5.24	9
Krypton	1.14	58
Xenon	0.086	51
Hydrogen	0.5	5
Acetylene	0.02	–

all the same intensity and the relatively few bright ones will tend to dominate the rest. Different amounts of energy are also required to stimulate the several gases of the atmosphere to emit light. In addition, different amounts of energy are required to excite a single atom depending upon whether it remains electrically neutral or loses one or more electrons. While these facts may appear to be complications, they will be seen to provide the necessary leverage to pry this subject apart.

If a gaseous mixture is exposed to a limited amount of energy, either thermal or electrical, only those atoms will begin to emit light for which the energy is sufficient. In other words, some gases are more easily stimulated than others depending upon an inherent sensitivity. The scientific measure of this threshold for each element is known as the ionization potential, that is, the minimum amount of energy required to lift an electron from its ground state to the next higher state. Light of a unique color is emitted when an electron fills the vacancy. Such data for the atmospheric gases are tabulated below.[13] These values pertain to free atoms whereas most gas atoms are bound together in pairs. The corresponding ionization potentials for the diatomic molecules is slightly different than the tabulated value but they will suffice for the present purpose.

	Ionization Potential (ev)*			
Gases	I**	II	III	IV
Nitrogen	14.53	29.59	47.43	77.45
Oxygen	13.61	35.11	54.89	77.39
Argon	15.76	27.62	40.9	59.79
Carbon Dioxide	–	–	–	–
Neon	21.56	41.07	63.5	97.02
Helium	54.48	54.56	–	–
Krypton	14.00	24.56	36.9	43.5
Xenon	12.13	21.2	31.2	42
Hydrogen	13.6	–	–	–
Acetylene	–	–	–	–

* Customarily expressed in electron volts where 1 ev = 1.602×10^{-12} erg.
** Roman numerals indicate: I, neutral atom; II, singly ionized; III, doubly ionized and so on.

As would be expected, the table shows in Column I that the amount of energy required to lift an electron to its next higher state is less than that required to remove it from the atom entirely as given in Column II. Naturally, even greater amounts of energy must be expended to remove a second, or a third, electron as shown in Columns III and IV. The most easily stimulated gas is seen to be xenon, having an ionization potential for the neutral atom of only 12.13 ev. Under normal conditions, the atmosphere is not luminous because less than 12.13 ev is available to the atoms. Suppose that by some unknown means, however, a UFO delivered a gradually increasing amount of energy to the gases surrounding it. At some point, the atmosphere would absorb enough energy to become luminous and the onset would correspond to the excitation of xenon. Further increases in energy transfer would activate the other gases in inverse order of their thresholds and their light would simply be added to that from xenon. Or if some sort of resonance phenomenon excited the various species individually, the atmosphere would take on a series of colors corresponding to each species. Some complex statistical and quantum mechanical aspects apply here but they need not be taken into account to develop the argument.

Well, if xenon is the most easily excited of the atmospheric gases, does it emit one or more colors that can be readily identified and, if so, have such colors been reported by the witnesses? The neutral atom of xenon emits three separate, but closely spaced, spectral lines in the center of the blue band of the spectrum. Thus light from xenon is seen as a pure, intense blue. It is strongly suspected, therefore, that xenon is responsible for the "blue," "brilliant blue," and "luminous blue" that were reported in the sample cases. The identity of xenon as the source seems to be almost assured because no other neutral gases in the atmosphere emit mid-blue photons. Considering the rarity of xenon, it is somewhat surprising that the evidence should point to it. At standard conditions of temperatures and pressure, air contains about 6.06×10^{23} molecules and free atoms in 22.4 liters. The proportion of xenon being 0.086 per 1,000,000 means that the density of xenon is about 2.3×10^{13} atoms per cubic centimeter, certainly an adequate supply.

In the following table, the three blue lines of xenon are plotted in the blue zone of the spectrum between wavelengths of 4240 and 4912 A°. Similar spectral lines from all other neutral gases in the atmosphere are similarly identified.[14] Their colors are indicated by their positions in relation to the standard color zones of the visible spectrum, usually taken as 4000 to 7000 A° (1 Angstrom = 10^{-8}cm). Some young people can detect ultraviolet in wavelengths as short as 3130 A°, although the faint images are not focused without special glasses.[15]

As the hypothetical UFO increased the transfer of energy to the atmosphere, other color contributions would appear. The "orange-red" or "fiery red" so frequently seen near UFOs can very probably be assigned to the brilliant orange-red of neon, 6402 A°, that is so easily recognized in neon signs. The combination of the green line of neon, 5401 A°, with the blue of xenon would yield the often reported "bluishgreen" or it may come from hydrogen, 4861 A°. "Purple" would result from the blue of xenon and the red of argon, 6965 A°. While these identifications are certainly not demonstrated, they tentatively suggest a plausible explanation for the variety of UFO colors.

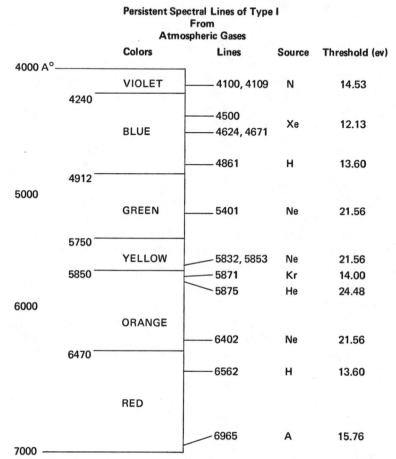

Persistent Spectral Lines of Type I
From
Atmospheric Gases

Colors	Lines	Source	Threshold (ev)
4000 A°			
VIOLET	4100, 4109	N	14.53
4240			
	4500	Xe	12.13
BLUE	4624, 4671		
	4861	H	13.60
4912			
5000			
GREEN	5401	Ne	21.56
5750			
YELLOW	5832, 5853	Ne	21.56
5850	5871	Kr	14.00
	5875	He	24.48
6000			
ORANGE			
	6402	Ne	21.56
6470			
	6562	H	13.60
RED			
	6965	A	15.76
7000			

It is noted with minor exceptions that the most likely candidates for color emission are helium, neon, argon, krypton, and xenon. It is precisely these noble gases that are favored for use in gaseous lasers. Almost all radiation from un-ionized noble gases in lasers, however, lies in the infrared or far-infrared. Only neon has a group of transitions emitting visible light. This group consists of seven lines with wavelengths between 5939 and 6401

A°, all within the orange zone. On the other hand, many spectral lines in the visible region are produced by ionized atoms of the noble gases, about 340 being known.[16]

An entirely different type of stimulated light emission that does not involve ionization occurs upon dissociation of atoms and molecules leaving the atom in an excited state.[17] As laser operation is critically dependent upon the geometry of apparatus and the pressure of the gases, usually very low, it is virtually impossible that any laser effect, per se, is involved in the luminosity of UFOs. The maser principle, however, may well prove to be the mechanism by which UFOs transfer energy to the atmosphere, namely, by electromagnetic energy of radio frequency or higher. Many clues along this line will be discovered in subsequent sections.

Dazzling Brightness

Sometimes the light emitted by a UFO is so intense that its surface is entirely obscured from view. Everything from "welding torch" to "burning magnesium" has been used to convey this idea. Direct and specific association with a metallic-appearing object has occurred when the source of light came down to the ground, dimmed, and revealed the material body of the UFO itself. Conversely, metallic constructions initially observed on the ground have become dazzling just before zooming out of sight.

The reference to "welding torch" justifies an examination of welding and related phenomena in the search for understanding the bright, white, UFO. The common welding torch burns a mixture of acetylene gas and oxygen at temperatures up to 6,000°F. Thermal agitation at such temperatures ionizes the gas molecules that, upon returning to the ground state, emit light copiously. The intensity may be so great that eyes must be shielded to avoid serious damage. Somewhat lower temperatures are achieved in electrical welding where a continuous arc is maintained between a welding rod and the work piece. The brilliant beam of a carbon-arc spotlight arises from the same process. More than 300 spectral lines in the visible region have been identified from such electrical sparks in air. Nearly all of them are emitted by the predominant gases, nitrogen, oxygen, and to a lesser extent, argon.[18] Collisions by electrons and thermal agitation of the gas molecules produce the requisite ionization. In summary, it is clear that these examples of gaseous luminosity depend upon high temperature, photon emission by the more abundant gases, and the mixture of numerous spectral lines to produce white light.

In addition to man-made sources, one can look to natural phenomena for further clues. In an ordinary bolt of lightning, the gas temperature is raised in a split second to about 25,000°C causing ionization of most of the gas atoms in its path.[19] Sudden expansion of the extremely hot gases sends the crashing sounds of thunder rolling across the countryside. The spectral composition of lightning flashes is typical of any electrical spark in air. The production of thunder is especially germane to this inquiry because UFOs are nearly always reported to be silent, or to make only a soft, hissing noise. A loud explosion is rarely heard from a UFO but not accompanying the standard flyby of an intensely luminous object. (See the chapter on Sounds.) It would appear that the blinding light emitted by UFOs is not associated with extremely high temperatures. Otherwise, thermal expansion of the gases would produce a horrendous racket, like continuous lightning. As no such sounds are reported, it may be concluded that the bright luminosity associated with UFOs is produced at very modest temperatures, compared to lightning.

Another natural phenomenon is also of interest, namely, balls of fire in the air that are known as ball lightning. They consist of brightly shining globules of gas whose sizes normally range between that of a grape and a grapefruit. They lazily drift a few meters off the ground for 1 to 5 seconds but some may last for a minute or so. The globe, or spheroid, typically emits a hissing sound, is not known to radiate heat although it may set fire to objects it touches, and it disappears either silently or with a loud report. This phenomenon has been observed since ancient times and it is thought to be fairly common.[20]

Nevertheless, most people would be very puzzled by a display of ball lightning. In the first place, it would remain unidentified, that is, obviously not a plane, bird, or balloon. Secondly, its drifting through the atmosphere would be properly denoted as "flying." Finally, it would be considered an object of some kind, in contrast to an hallucination, because it may have set fire to a henhouse when it entered through a crack in the door. In a very valid sense, therefore, ball lightning may be considered as an unidentified flying object. However, such an appraisal would have little direct bearing upon the study of UFOs as that term is being used here. Considering the similarities between ball lightning and UFOs as they are sometimes manifest, it is not surprising that the two should be occasionally confused or that reports of the former would show up in the UFO literature. These extraneous reports should obviously be sorted out and disregarded as some instances in the sample of sightings.[21] An attempt to explain the entire subject of UFOs as misinterpreted observations of ball lightning produced much valuable information on plasmas but was not very convincing.[22] However, an unsuspected and ironic relationship between these two subjects becomes apparent upon considering some details.

Numerous theories of ball lightning have been proposed but none thus far is capable of explaining all aspects of the subject. The most promising concept is that a plasma is initiated by the high-frequency, electromagnetic fields associated with ordinary lightning. Frequencies in the range of 100 to 4,000 MHz (million cycles per second) have been observed. While considerable ionization is present, some luminosity in the spheres may result from excited electronic levels not requiring ionization of the gases.[23]

It appears that absorption of energy elevates oxygen atoms to two, well-known, metastable states having decay times of 45 minutes and 8 seconds, respectively. Immediate decay is forbidden as the electrons are trapped in the excited state with the wrong spin. An intermolecular collision is required to deactivate the state through transfer of angular momentum thereby permitting release of the stored energy. It is then apparently transferred to carbon dioxide which immediately radiates it away in a continuous spectrum. Based upon collision rates at 2,000°F it has been estimated that these metastable states would be dissipated in one second, not inconsistent with the lifetime of ball lightning.

Various attempts have been made to estimate the temperature of the luminous gases. While a Russian investigator estimated 14,000°K for a yellow ball, other estimates are much lower. One observer concluded that the temperature was somewhat greater than 4,000°K based upon the concentrations of ozone and nitrogen dioxide measured in a trail left by a ball. The range of 4,000 to 5,000°C was inferred from Wein's law and the red and red-yellow colors commonly reported. Temperatures as low as 200°C have been considered. Because the witnesses have failed to report any sensation of heat near ball lightning, much preference should be given to the lower estimates. Ball lightning clearly involves a natural mechanism for producing bright luminosity of atmospheric gases at moderate temperatures and this mechanism may well account for the similar luminosity of UFOs.

As mentioned previously, ball lightning appears to be created and sustained by a supply of radiant energy in the frequency range of at least 100 to 4,000 MHz. This range is in the lower end of a zone of the electromagnetic spectrum from about 300 MHz to 300,000 MHz that is known as the microwave region. Lying between the bands used for radio broadcasting and the visible zone, it encompasses the frequencies used for microwave ovens, point-to-point telecommunications, radar, and special bands allocated by the Federal Communications Commission for industrial, scientific, and medical purposes. Most important among the latter are the frequencies of 915 and 2,450 MHz because available tubes, converting direct current to microwave energy at these frequencies, allow highpowered applications. For example, a klystron having an average power rating of 500 kW is manufactured.[24] It has been predicted that some similar devices operating in the frequency range of 1,000 to 3,000 MHz will ultimately be feasible at power levels approaching 10 MW.[25] At very low gas pressures, plasmas are easily created by the application of microwave energy. It has been observed in such a plasma that the sensible gas temperature was 700°K whereas the electron temperature exceeded 10,000°K[26] It seems quite likely that some such compound state exists within ball lightning and on the surface of UFOs when they are extremely bright. Ionization levels and luminosity would be very high while the gas temperature would remain relatively low. A plasma of this type could be sustained on the surface of a UFO only by a continuing absorption of microwave energy emitted by the UFO.

Fortunately, ball lightning can be studied in the laboratory. It was first created artificially by the Radio Frequency Company, Incorporated of Medfield, Massachusetts. Electromagnetic energy from a radio transmitter was injected into a large, aluminum box at resonant frequency. A ball of luminous gases about one foot in diameter suddenly formed and floated around inside the box until the power was turned off. In subsequent research at Brookhaven National Laboratory, similar plasmas have lived several seconds without power. It was suggested by the researchers that the radio-frequency energy was absorbed by nitrogen and oxygen and temporarily held in metastable states.[27]

Metastable states are thus seen to play a leading role in the existence and longevity of ball lightning. If the bright luminosity of UFOs depends upon the same physical processes, then some clues should be hidden in the UFO reports and photographs. A case in point may be the experience of a Brazilian woman, Mrs. de Mendonca, and her companions. At the end of a two-hour car chase, a Saturn-shaped UFO hovered close to the ground for about 15 minutes. An unspecified time later, the witnesses found an "odd luminous haze floating in the air above where the object had hovered" and they watched it slowly dissolve.[28] A similar detail was noted in a sighting of six UFOs in Argentina that, upon departing, left clouds of white smoke.[29] These observations suggest that the UFO charged the metastable states of atmospheric oxygen while hovering and, upon flying away, left them to decay gradually with the production of light.

In numerous photographs, UFOs are depicted with luminous tails that, heretofore, have been inexplicable.[30] By transferring energy to the atmosphere while traversing the sky, a UFO should leave a luminous wake where metastable states are decaying and transferring the stored energy to instantaneous, light emitters. Motion pictures of such tails should yield some quantitative data as the rate of energy transfer to the atmosphere, the speed of the UFO, and the length of the tail can be related with mathematical precision. It should be emphasized that intermolecular collisions are the controlling factor in releasing the stored energy and the rate of collisions is dependent upon the temperature and pressure. Because molecular agitation is diminished at low temperature, a cold day should retard the release of the states and increase the persistence of a UFO tail. Collision rates are also less frequent at low pressures, hence the tails should be especially persistent at high altitudes, having the compound advantage of frigidity and rarefaction. These considerations may suggest an interpretation of the prominent tail attached to a glowing, egg-shaped object that was photographed from earth orbit by the American astronaut, McDivitt.[31]

There exists yet another set of facts closely tying UFOs to ball lightning. Electrical discharges in the atmosphere initiate some important chemical changes. Energy states of atoms are modified and numerous chemical compounds are formed from the constituent gases. In a high-voltage spark, nitrogen is elevated to a metastable state having several interesting properties. It produces a soft, white glow that continues for some time after the electric discharge has been stopped. Such excited nitrogen is known chemically as "activated" because it will readily combine with many other elements whereas ordinary nitrogen will not.[32] It combines with hydrogen to form ammonia (NH_3) and with oxygen to form nitric oxide (NO). This oxide is quite stable at high temperatures but below 150°C it reacts with oxygen to form nitrogen dioxide (NO_2). The dioxide can react with still other atmospheric gases to form nitrobenzene ($C_6H_5NO_2$), an oily substance that is highly poisonous and has a strong odor like oil of bitter almonds. Also produced by electrical discharges is a highly reactive form of oxygen known as ozone (O_3) whose odor one learns to recognize in association with sparking, electrical apparatus.

While the sense of smell is not thoroughly understood, it is known to depend upon the molecular structure and chemical groups as a series of benzene derivatives have a similar odor. The nose is extremely sensitive, ethyl mercaptan being detectable down to concentrations as low as 4×10^{-8} milligrams per liter of air.[33] The above gases should be manufactured in an electrical discharge within ball lightning and they would not have to be present in large amounts to be noticed, that is, smelled by the witnesses. The odor of ball lightning is "usually described as sharp and repugnant, resembling ozone, burning sulphur or nitric oxide."[34] The reference to sulphur is readily understood as that element is a notorious air pollutant arising from automobile exhausts and smoke from industrial plants. Even in rural areas, the sulphur content of air may be quite high due to its production by bacteria in the mud of swamps and lake- and stream-bottoms.[35] While it may seem farfetched to inquire whether UFOs have any odor, it would be particularly significant if witnesses have detected those very gases that are produced in electrical discharges in direct association with them. One need only examine the record, as in the following tabulation, to see that such is the case.

Descriptions implying sulphur dioxide (SO_2) are the most numerous, however, benzene and its derivatives are mentioned. The term "pungent" and the reference to an electrical circuit almost assuredly implies ozone. At any rate, this evidence is an independent source of information that points to an electrical disturbance on the surface of UFOs that is undoubtedly associated with the luminosity.

Case No.	Description of Odor
51	strange cloying smell
72	pungent.
73	burning benzene
94	burning sulphur
101	unpleasant
102	ether mixed with sulphurous smoke, nauseous
199	nitrobenzene
584	sulphurous
615	powerful, enbalming fluid
616	strong unpleasant
684	burned gasoline
721	sulphur or rotten eggs
768	sulphur
832	sulphur and camphorated oil
844	burning electrical circuit
875	sulphur
879	strong, melted iron
909	strange, powerful

of this process and microwave energy is strongly implied by experimental data. Irradiation of various gases with microwaves produces a wide variety of gas atoms and free radicals, the required forms for chemical recombinations. In air, nitric oxide is produced. The efficiency of this reaction is greatly increased when the microwave energy is pulsed. Ethane and methane are decomposed into carbon and hydrogen but benzene is stable. In other words, a pulsed discharge of microwaves in air would suffice to generate nitric oxide and, in a subsequent reaction, the benzene that has been noted in the vicinity of UFOs.[36] As the benzene is not decomposed in the microwave field, any that were formed would accumulate then linger until detected. Oxidation of sulphur has also been accomplished in the laboratory with microwave irradiation, namely, conversion of sulphur dioxide to sulphur trioxide. Similar oxidation of atmospheric sulphur to sulphur dioxide could well be responsible for the commonly reported sulphurous odors.[37]

Sequential Multi-Colors

From the foregoing discussion it appears that energy originating in the UFOs is responsible for atmospheric luminosity in their immediate vicinity. Furthermore, various colors seem to be associated with different rates of energy transfer from UFOs to the atmosphere. Thus it might be possible to identify several energy states of UFOs that are distinguished by the character of the induced light. While certainly incomplete, energy states are tentatively assigned as follows:

State	Appearance	Physical Basis
0	Metallic	Energy inadequate to excite perceptible light
1	Blue Glow	Excitation of xenon only
2	Orange-red	Selective exitation of neon
3	White Glow	Decay of metastable nitrogen
4	Brilliant White	Limited ionization of all gases augmented by the "ball lightning mechanism"

If such categories are real, one would expect to find some correlation between the color of a UFO and its pattern of flight, a relationship that was observed at least as early as 1956.

> The colors mentioned seem associated in some way with the speed, or more probably with the rate of acceleration. The silvery grey with an aureole of dark red is seen when the object is stationary or traveling very slowly. Then comes the vivid red . . . At high acceleration the white, green, blue and purple appear."[38]

Very little progress in understanding this relationship has been made, however, the present model may be helpful.

When two people got out of their car to watch an object hovering at ground level, "its color changed from orange to fluorescent green before it took off."[39] Apparently State 2 prevailed while the object was stationary and the change preceded the acceleration. The original orange color must have been produced by photons having wave lengths between 5850 A° and 6470 A°. Similarly, the green color necessarily arose from wave lengths between 4912 A° and 5750 A°. Photons producing a green sensation, being of shorter wave lengths, are more energetic than their yellow cousins. Thus the change from orange to green implies an increase in the energy emitted by the atoms. From the above definitions of the color bands, one can easily calculate the minimum and maximum energy changes that might occur, assuming constant intensity. The color changes would be accomplished by an increase of about 5 to 24 percent. It is suspected that the orange color derived from neon at 6402 A°. But neon also has a prominent line in the green at 5401 A°. If these wave lengths were involved, the energy increase would amount to about 16 percent. That the UFO began pumping more energy into the atmosphere as it accelerated is clear. But further analysis is frustrated by complications such as the absorption efficiency of the atoms for an unknown mechanism, transition probabilities within the emitting atoms, and the variable sensitivity of the human eye to different colors. Although green is frequently observed, it has not been possible to assign a meaningful UFO state number to it.

A man saw a luminous, oval object rising from the flat roof of his house, "varying in colour between white and red."[40] Very little detail is available in this report and it cannot be determined whether white to red was the sequence of color change or whether the transition occurred several times in reversing order. At least it shows a color change associated with ascension.

An oval object followed a woman driving her car for 13 kilometers. Its "color suddenly changed from reddish-orange to bluish-white before accelerating out of sight."[41] As a prelude to acceleration, this UFO "stepped on the gas" and moved from State 2 to State 4. The "bluish" component is appropriate to State 4 as a welding arc has such a cast.

An object shaped like two plates glued together with an oval on top hovered at treetop level over a man's car for two minutes. "It took a 45° inclination, rose, made a right angle turn, and changed color (white to yellow to blue to green) as it accelerated."[42]

Again, a brilliant color display occurs upon acceleration. The corresponding States, 4-2-1-?, seem to be appropriate to a gradual reduction of power in approaching cruising speed.

Following a chase by a glowing object at 170 km/hr, a witness stopped his car to watch. "The color changed in sequence, orange to red to blue to green, and the object wobbled on its axis" as the object came from 100 meters to within 30 meters. It then suddenly left straight up.[43] The energy states, 3-2-1-?, are seemingly appropriate to deceleration during the close approach. The transition of blue to green is puzzling.

A lighted object in the sky was observed to be going up and down; its color "turning from white to greenish-blue."[44] Again, the description is not explicit enough to determine if the color change was repeated and synchronized with the changes in altitude, or if a gradual change occurred throughout the sighting. In the former interpretation, alternation between States 3 and 1 would make sense.

Four boys observed a cone-shaped object descending with an oscillating motion. It has "a blue underside, and a top that changed from red to orange to white."[45] The last change, corresponding to States 2-3, implies an increase in power for deceleration.

Every instance of sequential color change in the sample cases was associated with accelerations and the energy state model. Rough as it is, this association seems to make this perplexing aspect of UFOs more meaningful. This correlation is critically important as it establishes a relationship between the UFO propulsion system and the stimulation of atmospheric gases to emission of light. A great deal of work in this area is certainly needed and a thorough analysis of the better documented cases by a theoretical spectroscopist should bring it into sharp focus.

Although no source for green light was suggested above, a likely candidate is neon with its spectral line at 5401 A°. The logical difficulty of positively identifying neon is the relatively high energy required for excitation, being the same as that for its orange-red line. The latter would be expected to dominate and obscure the green. Obviously, only a partial solution to this problem can be offered now. A similar uncertainty prevails for the often-noted, bluish-green color for which two possible sources are in contention. A commercial laser based upon argon emits a bluish-green light having wave lengths in the range of 4579-5145 A°, mid-blue to about mid-green, although spectral lines in that range for argon are not tabulated in the literature.[46] As argon is fairly abundant in air, these lasing transitions could account for this color. A competing possibility is the bluish-green line of hydrogen at 4861 A° whose low threshold makes it easy to stimulate. One problem is that free hydrogen in the atmosphere is very rare, less than one part per million. But each molecule of water vapor in the atmosphere, containing two atoms of hydrogen, assures an adequate supply. The concentration of hydrogen would be greatest on damp, rainy or foggy days, when the relative humidity is 100% and the air is filled with water droplets. If it were found that the bluish-green color were more pronounced during inclement weather, the source might be pinpointed to hydrogen. But no such correlation has been attempted. UFOs frequently take refuge in clouds whose moisture content is substantially greater than the surrounding air. This circumstance affords some opportunity to detect light emission from hydrogen if it is significant. From statements of the witnesses, it is apparent that clouds become luminous when they are entered by a UFO and the color has been called "unusual."[47] At least once it was observed to be "green"[48] and no conflicting reports have been encountered. It seems that hydrogen probably contributes to the colorful display from UFOs but it may share the credit for bluish-green with argon.

Simultaneous Multi-Colors

In addition to UFOs exhibiting several colors one after another during maneuvers, they are sometimes seen to produce several colors at the same time. In one instance the underside remained blue whereas the colors on top changed.[49] Horizontal bands of color on another object were "blue, red and green."[50] These cases are not very instructive but they may point to a highly selective mechanism for stimulating the emission of light, probably from the noble gases. Horizontal disposition of the bands on an axially symmetric object may reflect geometrical features that would alter or distort electromagnetic fields in their vicinity. Perhaps that might be the explanation for a "six story" object from which rainbow colors poured off its edges "like water."[51]

Other Lighting Details

Apart from the diffuse luminosity, UFOs are frequently observed to carry ordinary "navigation" lights. One of the most common features is a prominent light on the top which may be of any color, either steady or flashing. Other lights are sometimes distributed over the surface, typically at the ends of elongated objects or along the periphery and on the bottom of discs. These lights vary greatly in number and color and, in the sample cases, have no discernible significance. Usually, two or more lights of different colors are reported; one object was estimated to have about 30 lights. Nearly all colors are reported, most often red, blue, white, yellow, orange and green. Some are steady while others are flashing. This display has been aptly compared to a "Christmas tree."

Another type of illumination less common than surface lights consists of one or more powerful beams resembling searchlights. They are used for scanning the countryside, pointing directly downward or upward, or at houses and vehicles. By switching a vertical beam on and off, an object on the ground seemed to signal another one at high altitude which answered in the same manner.[52] Red, white, blue and green beams have been reported.

Finally, about a dozen witnesses reported "windows," "portholes," "openings" or "doors" through which poured bright light, most commonly with a yellow to orange tinge. Individual lights and general illumination have also been observed through transparent domes atop disc-shaped objects.

*A new fact is battling strenu-
ously for access to your ears. A
new aspect of the universe is
striving to reveal itself. But no
fact is so simple that it is not
harder to believe than to doubt
at the first presentation.*
— *Lucretius*

CHAPTER 4

SOUNDS

Whether hovering motionless, gliding along at tree-top level, or
cruising across the sky, UFOs are notably silent. Astonished
witnesses often report that they were certainly close enough to
have heard a conventional aircraft. Of course, they expected to
hear the sounds generated by the engines, jet exhaust, or propel-
lers, all of which are associated with the means of flight. The lack
of such sounds from UFOs clearly indicates that their propulsion
systems are unique and unconventional. Even at supersonic
speeds, when airplanes invariably produce sonic booms, UFOs
remain silent. A physical basis for this unusual performance will
become apparent in a later chapter. While the familiar noise of
flight is not associated with UFOs, they are known to produce
some sounds. In 103 instances of close encounters during the
decade 1958-68, witnesses reported hearing sounds and attempted to describe them.[1] As sounds are very difficult to describe, it
is not surprising to find that a wide variety of expressions were
used. Imagine the sound of a quarter dropping into a coffee can
and the numerous adjectives or comparisons that would be
evoked from several people in the next room. Further suppose
that several different sounds occurred simultaneously, such as

slamming a car door and spinning a New Year's noise-maker. Several people called upon to describe this racket would produce a bewildering assortment of words. A reasonable understanding of what they were trying to communicate would require that expressions pertaining to each component of the sounds first be isolated. Then some concept of the sources could be developed from the various expressions and allusions for each component.

While some of the adjectives used by witnesses, such as "dull" and "strange," are essentially without meaning, most of them can be associated with a limited number of different sounds having distinctive characteristics. The following table organizes nearly all the statements by the witnesses into five general categories depending upon the type of sounds that they attempted to describe.

Violent	Low Pitch	Rush of Air	High Pitch	Signals
bang	hum	whoosh	shrill whir	beeping
loud explosion	low pitch hum		high pitch	modulating whistling
thundering roar	low buzz	swishing	high pitched hum	signal-like noise
deafening roar	humming	rushing	high speed drill	strange pulsing
shock wave	buzzing	hissing	shrieking	shrill beeping
blast	swarm of bees	wings	strong whistling	
roar	humming bees	fluttering	loud turbine	
	generator		whine	
	electric motor		piercing whistle	
	whirring		jet	
	strange vibrations		whistling	
			painful	
			truck on wet pavement	

transformer and wind   vacuum cleaner

whistling, roar and bangs

It is interesting and reassuring that the descriptions by three witnesses encompassed combinations of the selected categories. For example, an allusion to a "vacuum cleaner" clearly refers to the combination of the noise from rushing air and the high-pitched whine of a turbine. These combinations are designated in the table by lines curving upward toward the appropriate category.

Violent Noises

Two subtypes of violent sounds are clearly discerned—an instantaneous explosion like a shock wave and a loud, continuous noise. These occurred as "it touched the ground," "upon rising" from a low altitude, during "30 seconds before takeoff," and as a UFO "left with a roar and a series of bangs." It appears that these sounds are directly related to the application of power for rapid acceleration or deceleration but they should not be confused with the normally silent landing and liftoff. A large UFO at a distance of 700 meters from a witness was slowly cruising at an estimated 80 km/hr, certainly subsonic; about three seconds after an intense blue light came on, the witness heard a "shock wave."[2] If the blue light generated a compression wave, it would travel at approximately 1100 ft/sec and reach the witness in just over two seconds. This internal consistency supports a general association between the blue light and the shock wave and the technical implications will be explored later in an analysis of propulsion.

Humming

The second category of sounds, typified as humming, denotes a low level that would not be heard at great distances. The allusion to bees is significant as it provides a specific basis for estimating the frequency or pitch of the sound. Of course, the humming noise of a flying bee comes from the wing beat of about 270 times per second,[3] corresponding closely to the musical note of middle C. Much lower tones, also referred to as humming, are generated by hummingbirds, specifically for the ruby-throated variety, at 70 beats per second for the female and 50 for the smaller male.[4] These tones correspond approximately to the C below the bass clef and the next lower G. They are certainly consistent with the

60—or 120—cycle hum produced by electrical apparatus mentioned by several witnesses. It would seem farfetched to search for other causes of this sound when electrical machinery will do so nicely. In view of the brightly lighted interior of UFOs, their numerous navigation lights, and occasional intense beams, a source of electrical power is required. One witness might even be taken at his word, namely, it sounded like a "generator."

Implied in the discussion thus far is the assumption that witnesses heard the humming sound in the normal fashion, namely, by the pressure of sound waves on the eardrum being transmitted by the bony structure of the inner ear to stimulate the auditory nerve. Any possible alternatives should be taken into account. It was suggested previously that UFOs emit high frequency, electromagnetic radiation that, like radar, would have no effect upon the eardrum. However, medical experiments have shown that some people can hear modulated, radio-frequency energy that they interpret as a "buzzing or knocking" sound. All subjects felt that the sound originated behind their heads regardless of the actual location.[5] Apparently, the pulsed energy bypasses the ear structure and induces signals directly in the auditory nerve. The physical reality of this mechanism was demonstrated when microelectrodes were inserted into a single nerve fiber with subsequent exposure to microwaves, electromagnetic energy in the range of 200 to 3,000 megacycles per second. Electrical potentials from millivolts up to 0.10 volts were measured between the inside and outside of the surface membrane.[6] As these tests were conducted with modulated microwaves it is obvious that the subjects were sensing the pulses of energy, not the carrier frequency. Pulse repetition rates as low as 160 per second are used on the FPS16 radar at Jodrell Bank, England,[7] and rates as low as 300 per second appear to be common.[8] Thus the buzzing sound heard from UFOs may be stimulated directly within the head of the witnesses by high-frequency radiation being pulsed at a low, audio rate.

In passing, it is noted that voice modulation of microwaves might be developed to communicate with totally deaf people whose ear structure has been destroyed but whose auditory nerve is still intact. Should such prove to be possible and safe, one could also transmit a voice signal some distance on a microwave beam to a person without an electronic receiver. As shall be seen later, something like this may be a part of the total UFO phenomenon.

Rush of Air

Now to the third category of UFO sounds, something similar to the rush of air. Because of the consistency of the descriptions, the sound seems to be well-enough identified but there are no clues to its cause. At this stage of investigation, it can only be guessed that the sound is emitted by agitated molecules in an ionized "skin effect" on the surface of the vehicle. In the electrical breakdown of air along a high-voltage transmission line, called corona, a glow can be seen in the dark and a "hissing" sound becomes audible.[9] A similar electrical discharge may account for the sound of this general type.

High Pitch

It would be of interest and possible value to establish an approximate frequency range for the sound that is characterized by high pitch. At first glance, a "truck on wet pavement" seems to offer little help but it is a useful springboard for understanding the intent of the witness in technical terms. This vague reference is assuredly related to the reaction of the tire tread on the road surface. In seeking a technical interpretation, it can be estimated that the characteristic dimension between elements of a typical tread is one-half inch, that a medium-sized truck has tires of about 3-ft diameter, and that the witness is referring to the nominal speed such as 40 m/hr. Under these conditions, the tread elements would impact upon, and release from, the roadway about 1,400 times per second, creating a moderately high-pitched tone roughly equivalent to the F one octave above the treble clef. This value can only be considered as a crude estimate as it could easily be off by a factor of 2 to 3 in either direction.

Many of the expressions used to describe this sound, "shrieking," "piercing whistle," and "whine" bring to mind the distressing noise of a jet aircraft as the engines are revved up to taxi away from a loading area or in preparation for take-off. This impression is strongly reinforced by explicit comparisons such as "loud turbine" and even "jet." Apparently the witnesses were attempting to describe the high-pitched scream of the engine rather than the roar of exhaust gases.

Most of the offensive noise from jets is generated by the high-speed rotation of the first stage compressor. It consists of a broad spectrum of noise plus several discrete frequencies related to the engine parts and their speed of rotation. A principal source of discrete frequencies is the siren interaction of the inlet guide vanes and the first stage rotor blades. The fundamental frequency can be calculated as the product of the number of blades on the rotor times its speed of rotation. Typically, 30 blades at 10,000 rpm would produce a fundamental of 5,000 cycles per second. In addition, low-order harmonics of significant intensity could be generated with frequencies up to about 12,000 cycles per second. Thus the high-pitched noise of jet engines is composed of several discrete frequencies in the range of 5,000 to 12,000 cycles per second superimposed upon a broad-band background.[10] Tones corresponding to these discrete frequencies, which are very high, can be described accurately as a "whine" or, for the higher ranges, a "whistle." As a point of reference, a 10-kc whistle can sometimes be heard between stations on AM radio.

As the sound heard by one witness reminded him of a "high-speed drill," another basis for estimating the frequency is available. Most high-speed drills are driven by electric motors at about 25,000 rpm, or 420 revolutions per second.[11] Fans are normally attached to the spindle for cooling the motor windings, with 15 blades being typical for small sizes. Thus the fundamental frequency from the fan would be about 6,300 cycles per second, not at all inconsistent with previous estimates. Other drill components, such as gears and bit, are reduced in speed by as much as 10 to 1 but are not notable noise generators.

From these data one may say that UFOs emit high-pitched sounds in the frequency range of about 1,000 to 10,000 cycles per second, probably consisting of several discrete frequencies. All indications are that the sound is caused by rotating machinery and, in particular, by blades attached thereto. In the absence of contrary indications, one would be tempted to guess that the machinery is somehow related to the propulsion system, but definitely not in the sense of ordinary jets. It might be pointed out that high-frequency sounds are significantly absorbed by the atmosphere, whereas low frequencies are practically unaffected; both are subject to attenuation according to the inverse square law. Atmospheric absorption at 8,000 cycles per second varies from 5 to 10 db per 100 meters, depending upon the temperature and humidity.[12] This selective absorption may explain why the high-pitch component is heard only at close range.

Coded Signals

Strange, signal-like sounds were reported in seven of the 447 close-encounter cases being analyzed. Perusal of the listed expressions suggests that "beeping" is the most descriptive term for this sound. While appearing only once in the above list, it was used on three separate occasions. Simultaneous radio interference was sometimes mentioned although it cannot be confirmed that the strange sound was actually emitted by the radios. In fact, radios were probably not involved. A 10-year-old boy saw a bright, silvery object standing on four legs in a wheat field. He heard a beeping sound just before the object rose from the ground and departed straight up. No radio is mentioned in the report and it seems unlikely that the boy had one in a wheat field. Another similar instance occurred on a beach when a man heard a "modulated whistling" as an object rose off the sand to a height of 20 meters.

In the famous case of Mr. and Mrs. Barney Hill,[13] "beeping" sounds played an unusually significant role. While on vacation trip through New Hampshire, the Hills saw a large UFO approach from great distance and hover low over a field. Barney, who was driving, stopped the car and got out. Overcome with curiosity, he walked toward the UFO until he could see people inside and, with binoculars, could make out a pair of strange eyes staring at him. He fled in terror. The UFO followed their car for some time as the Hills tried to keep it in sight, excitedly discussing their predicament and experiencing a premonition that the people in the UFO would try to capture them.

> Then suddenly a strange electronic beeping was heard. The car seemed to vibrate with it. It was in irregular rhythm—beep, beep—beep, beep, beep—seeming to come from behind the car, in the direction of the trunk.[14]

Since the apparent source of the sound was behind the Hills, it could not have come from a radio. When asked if the radio was on at the time, Barney replied

> No. My radio was not on. It was so late, and I did not think I could get a station. So when I left Canada, I cut my radio off. . . .I don't play my radio when I'm driving.[15]

Upon hearing the "beeping" sound, the Hills experienced an odd drowsiness. Sometime later, a second series of beeps returned them to normal. They were unaware of anything between the two series of beeps. Much later, however, intervening events were recalled under hypnosis. The Hills had been captured by occupants of the UFO, taken aboard a gigantic vehicle, and subjected to biomedical experiments for nearly two hours. The Hills had fallen under control of the aliens at the first series of beeps. They were released with a posthypnotic suggestion that they would not remember anything about their experience, then awakened with the second series of beeps.

The onset of amnesia in another case was also triggered by beeping sounds.[16] A police officer in Nebraska approached to within 14 meters of a UFO on the highway and heard a shrill, beeping sound. He judged that it took only 10 minutes to return to headquarters, although one-half hour had elapsed. Under hypnosis at the University of Colorado, he recalled the events during the 20-minute period of amnesia. A very small person walked toward him from under the UFO and said that he had come to earth from outer space.[17] It may be assumed that the police officer was monitoring his radio at the time of encounter. However, the similarity of his experience with that of the Hills leads one to suspect that the radio was not involved in transmittal of the beeps.

It appears that beeping sounds near UFOs need not, and probably do not, involve radios, and that they are used to induce hypnotic trances, sometimes subjecting the witness to complete control by the UFO pilots. The mechanism for transmittal of the beeps seems to be encoded signals on a high-frequency carrier in the microwave range as suggested by the correlation between the Hills' experience and laboratory experiments on human subjects. Possible use of this mechanism that is more sophisticated than raw beeps is treated in a section on language and communication.

*The prospect of being wrong
need not frighten us a bit.*
— *Alan E. Nourse*

CHAPTER 5

ELECTRICAL INTERFERENCE

UFOs have been notorious for stopping automobiles at close range. It is relatively common for a motorist, cruising down the highway, to have his engine sputter, lose power, or stop running. At night, the headlights frequently grow dim or go out completely. Also, static is heard on the radio, and it may stop playing. The driver stops at the side of the road and gets out to search for the cause. Only then does he notice a large, glowing disc nearby, commonly hovering at low altitude over his car.

These effects are not limited to automobiles, but occur with all kinds of vehicles that are powered by internal combustion engines, except diesels. Incidents of engine interference or failure have been reported for aircraft, motorcycles, trucks, buses, power mowers, tractors, and other farm machinery. In all cases, the engines ran normally after the UFO had departed.

A list of 106 cases of electromagnetic interference by UFOs has been compiled.[1] These examples occurred at scattered locations in North America, South America, Europe, and Australia from August 1945 to November 1963. The age of these reports need not cause concern because they are thoroughly typical of many similar events of more recent years.

In this list, more than sixty vehicles are reported to have had their engines miss, lose power, or fail completely during the sighting. Simultaneous interference on the radio and/or fading or complete loss of headlights is common. Unfortunately, there is insufficient data to identify the cases that occurred in the daytime when headlights would not be turned on. Nor is it clear in which cases the vehicle was equipped with a radio, or whether any radio was being played. At first glance, the list appears to provide information regarding the relative susceptibility of engines, radios, and headlights to interference by UFOs. One would expect, for example, that upon approaching a UFO a driver would observe the loss of his radio, headlamps, and engine, in that order. But such is not the case. In three instances, the engine, radio, and lights were all affected; in two cases, they all failed, in the third, the engine and radio failed, but the lights only dimmed. While this last case suggests that lights may be the most resistant to UFO interference, several counter-examples belie this notion. In some cases, the lights dimmed or failed while the engine was unaffected. Thus the engines, radios, and lights appear to be roughly equal in their sensitivity to UFOs, a rather surprising observation in view of the extreme sensitivity of radios to ordinary electrical interference. Driving close to power transmission lines which operate at 60 cycles/second usually causes static on the radio without affecting the lights and engine. The implication is clear: the mechanism of UFO interference is something other than low frequency, electromagnetic radiation.

Close examination of the reported cases discloses a gradation effect and suggests that the influence on the vehicle is related to the strength of emanation or proximity to the UFO. One engine missed as the lights flickered—another engine sputtered as the lights only dimmed—a third engine ran normally as static was heard on the radio and the lights dimmed. An expected pattern thus emerges. A weak influence from a UFO at a great distance mildly disturbs the engine, radio, and lights, whereas a stronger influence upon closer approach causes all three to fail completely. In a previous chapter it was shown that the intensity of the field radiated by UFOs was also variable; hence, the graduated response could occur while the distance to the UFO remained fixed.

Internal Combustion Engines

As everyone knows, the common automotive engine operates by drawing air and vaporized gasoline into a combustion chamber where the mixture is ignited with an electrical spark. Disruption of a running engine by an object at some distance must effectively interfere with the fuel, air, or spark, or any combination thereof. The flow of both fuel and air is a consequence of the piston evacuating the cylinder and drawing air through the carburetor, where it picks up minute droplets of fuel. These functions must continue as long as a vehicle is moving and in gear, whether or not the engine is delivering power. In other words, these two essential functions of a running engine which is pulling a heavy vehicle cannot be stopped by any means short of physically halting the vehicle, like against a concrete overpass. The only way to stop a running engine, therefore, is to disrupt the electrical system. Thus the influence of UFOs upon automobiles is most assuredly electrical or electromagnetic in nature. This inference, based on the effects upon radios, is surely correct. Any doubt on this point is completely dispelled by an unlikely coincidence in Italy in 1954 when a UFO flew over a conventional tractor and a diesel tractor running side by side. The conventional tractor was stopped, but the diesel was not.[2] Similarly in England, the driver of a truck told the police that a hovering UFO knocked out his lights and radio while his diesel engine continued to run.[3]

The above line of reasoning may seem to be very elementary, but it was by no means obvious to the Condon Committee.[4] The primary effort of that investigation into the interference with engines was directed toward experimentally determining the effect of strong magnetic fields upon the components of the electrical system. In very strong fields up to 20,000 gauss, insignificant effects were measured for the spark plugs, battery, and lamp filaments. For the common steel encased coil, the spark was occasionally interrupted at 20,000 gauss. It was concluded that in view of "the magnetic shielding action of the sheet steel in the car body, the strength of the field outside the car would have to be considerably greater than this." Such strong fields would permanently alter the normal magnetic pattern of the car body. Hence, a car exposed to a strong magnetic field supposedly surrounding a UFO would carry a record of the event. Tests were conducted on a car that was alleged to have been stopped by a UFO. Its magnetic pattern was essentially the same as that of another car of the same make and model. The inquiry was dropped at that point with the conclusion that the car had not been exposed to an intense magnetic field. The implication was that it had not been exposed to a UFO, but of course, it may well have been stopped by a UFO without experiencing a strong magnetic field.

Instead of focusing exclusively upon strong magnetic fields, the investigation should have encompassed fluctuating, electromagnetic fields that could have effects upon engines, radios, and headlamps without altering the magnetic signature of the car body. This approach was suggested by David R. Saunders, who held a key position on the project.[5] High-frequency electromagnetic radiation is an excellent candidate for the cause of UFO interference with cars. It might be found capable of inducing hign-voltage surges in the secondary winding of the coil. The resulting sparks in the cylinders would be completely out of time with the sequence of events required for an engine to run. Timing of the spark is quite critical; an engine will not run if it is only slightly off timing. This mechanism might explain why engines seem to be unusually sensitive to UFO interference. Regarding radios, it is clear that a high frequency field could cause static, or if strong enough, saturate the input circuit, thereby blocking its normal reception. A physical basis for the effect upon headlamps is the increase of resistivity of tungsten in the presence of microwave energy.[6] Increasing resistance would reduce the flow of current through the lamp filament thereby diminishing the heating. The lamp would grow dim as the temperature dropped, or become entirely extinguished when the current became too low to keep the filament incandescent.

The "tungsten" effect offers an alternative explanation for engine failure also, in that distributor points, being made of tungsten alloy, would be subject to interference. An increase of resistance would reduce the current in the primary winding of the coil, thus reducing the spark intensity in the secondary winding or eliminating it altogether. As the distributor cap enclosing the points is non-metallic, the absence of good shielding could make the ignition system extremely sensitive to this mechanism. Two more incidental effects, related to vehicles, that must be accounted for by a valid interpretation are a wildly oscillating behavior of both ordinary compasses and magnetic speedometers.

Radios

As mentioned in the previous section, automobile radios, and those installed in other vehicles, such as aircraft, have been disrupted on many occasions by UFOs. It may be assumed that most of them were amplitude modulation (AM) sets, as prior to the midsixties frequency modulation (FM) receivers in automobiles were comparatively rare. Among the thirty-two cases of radio interference in the Hall list, some did not fail completely but emitted "static," "shrieking," "pulsating," and "roaring." Others produced intelligible signals such as "steady dit-dit-dit," "loud beeping," and "steady dot-dot-dash." Two such sounds were produced by radios in police cars. It appears that standard AM receivers are merely disrupted, whereas a message content is detected in the bandwidth commonly used for police communication. Again, an unusual coincidence provides some confirmation. In November 1957, a Canadian observed the simultaneous failure of his battery radio and a portable shortwave radio as a UFO hovered at low altitude. The regular portable simply failed, but "a single tone was heard on one shortwave frequency."[7]

While the radio interference and the sighting were simultaneous, there is no indication in these cases that the recognizable signals were emitted by the UFO, and there is ample reason to suspect that they were not. Nearly all medium-power marine beacons used for radio navigation, broadcast a steady repetition of dot-dash signals corresponding to a single letter in International Morse Code. A few coastal beacons transmit only a series of dashes, and are sometimes referred to as "beepers."[8] Aeronautical beacons, on the other hand, transmit coded signals of three letters, such as SFO for San Francisco.[9] Hence, the question arises as to whether one can identify marine beacons that are responsible for the above signals, namely,

Signal	Letter	Vicinity
. . .	S	Kodiak, Alaska
beeping	none	Hammond, Indiana
. . —	U	Hobbs, New Mexico

If such exist, they would be tabulated in *Radio Navigational Aids,* Publication No. 117-A and 117-B, U.S. Navy Hydrographic Office.

The inference to be drawn here relates to the mechanism of UFO interference. Rather than saturate or block the input circuit, radiant energy from the UFO may be disturbing the highly sensitive tuning adjustment, that is, by detuning the station from that to which it had been previously set. Thus police radios might be picking up signals from the marine band where standard broadcast receivers usually do not. This possibility seems all the more likely from the nearness of the police and marine bands. It seems odd, however, that car radios are not reported to have changed their stations.

The question remains, "How could such a change occur?" The answer may lie in the characteristics of a tuning circuit which is composed of a coil, capacitor, and resistor in series. When stimulated by an alternating voltage, the circuit carries an alternating current of the same frequency. The magnitude of the current depends upon the frequency, and it reaches a maximum when the stimulating frequency matches the natural, resonant frequency of the circuit. The frequency at which resonance occurs is governed by the values of the electrical elements in the circuit. Hence, the resonant frequency can be changed by modifying one of them; the set is usually tuned by adjusting the capacitance. A particular station is tuned in by adjusting the resonant frequency to correspond to its transmitted carrier. Competing signals from other stations are suppressed because they are out of resonance.[10]

Should the coil in the tuned circuit be exposed to a fluctuating field of high frequency, extraneous currents will be induced in it, thereby altering its normal role in the cirucit. Theoretically, the circuit would continue to function but at a different resonant frequency. In other words, the set would be detuned from the original station and might pick up another one. This mechanism of detuning may account for the common report of radio transmission being lost from aircraft, police cars, and radio stations. Police chasing a UFO in Danville, Illinois, were *unable to notify headquarters* because their radio went mysteriously dead.[11] Possibly their transmitter was detuned so that they could not be heard on the normally operating receiver at headquarters some distance away.

The most common problem with radios, however, is that they simply fail. They cease to produce any sounds in the presence of UFOs. Their return to normal after the UFO disappears weakens the notion that loss of power might be responsible. Any other possible basis for this behavior should be identified. As the influence of microwaves upon tungsten came under suspicion previously, it is rather significant to note that another major application of that metal is for cathodes in radio tubes.[12] Electrons inside the evacuated space of a radio tube are supplied by the cathode; they are boiled off its surface in vast numbers when it is at high temperature, producing the familiar glow in radio tubes. The flow of these electrons through the tube, being easily controlled, accounts for the extreme sensitivity of radios. In other words, signals are amplified enormously by controlling the flow of electrons through the tube. Restricting their supply at the origin, the cathode, would have a profound effect. It would reduce the normal gain through the tube, or in the limit, stop the current completely. The output of the radio would either diminish below the threshold for hearing or cease altogether until the normal conditions were restored. This behavior is precisely the expected consequence of increasing the resistance of the tungsten or tungsten-alloy cathode with microwaves. Cathodes are maintained at their operating temperature by a separate, low-voltage circuit. Current through that circuit heats the cathode to incandescence in an exact analogy to the filament in a headlamp.[13] Increasing the resistance in the circuit would reduce the current and the rate of heating, thereby reducing or shutting off the supply of electrons. This mechanism would also hamper or prevent broadcasting of messages on transmitters by restricting the internal amplification or limiting the flow of power through output tubes into the antenna.

Household Receivers and Lamps

Hall cited eighteen cases of interference with radios, television sets, and house lights as UFOs flew over cities, towns, and populated areas. Interference with television was six times more frequent than with radios, a ratio so great that an explanation should be sought. It may simply reflect the greater popularity of television, but some technical aspects are implied. The large, rooftop antennas commonly used for TV are much more efficient than the small, ferrite antennas that are built into table-model and portable radios. This factor alone could account for the observations. In addition, the UFO interference may have frequency components closer to that of the TV carriers than to that of radio.

In any event, the specific nature of the reported TV interference, such as "dimmed," "blurred," "loss of audio," and "distortion," indicates that the trouble was not caused by loss of power. Thus, one must look to direct interference in the receiver circuits along the lines described above. A few instances of household lights being dimmed or extinguished may be identical to the effect on automobile headlamps. Obviously, loss of electrical power could be responsible, and UFO interference with power transmission over large areas is another prominent feature of the whole problem.

Power Transmission

An association between UFOs and electrical power facilities has been recognized for many years. UFOs tend to hover near generating stations, switchyards, and substations, and to travel along the rights-of-way for high-voltage transmission lines. They are frequently seen at these locations at the time of, or just prior to, electrical blackouts over extended areas served by the facilities. Naturally, blame for the inconvenience is laid upon the UFOs, but satisfactory explanations have not been found. The deficiency is twofold: The affinity of UFOs for electrical facilities is not well understood and their method of causing power failure has not been satisfactorily identified.

During the fall of 1966, a series of UFO sightings in southern New Hampshire attracted the attention of a famous journalist who conducted a thorough, on-the-spot investigation. Armed with portable tape recorders, he collected testimony from many witnesses, some of which was later published verbatim. In 73 separate testimonies, a direct relationship was reported between the UFOs and the power lines of the Northeast Grid.[14] The UFOs typically appeared at low altitude near the transmission lines, alternately rising and falling behind the trees. On more than one occasion, a "pipelike object came down from the base of the disc and actually touched the lines, remaining there for a minute or so."[15] In view of such observations, the contention that these UFOs were merely some obscure, electrical blobs that were precipitated by the power lines is absolutely untenable, especially since many of them were also seen at great altitudes being chased by jet fighter planes. Since in thousands of other situations, UFOs have been well removed from transmission lines, this group of sightings, is unique and reveals a particular purpose behind their behavior. Exactly what this purpose might be is still an open question.

During the period of these sightings, on November 9, 1966, the power distribution system serving one-fifth of the American population in eight eastern states simply failed. The source of the trouble was initially reported to be a remote-controlled substation at Clay, New York, where only seconds before the blackout a pilot saw a brilliant, red ball, 100 feet in diameter. A total of five people saw this object, or one like it, in the vicinity. Investigations by the Federal Power Commission, however, officially traced the source of the blackout to a Canadian hydroelectric plant on the Niagara River. "The initial event was the operation of a backup relay at Beck Generating Station which opened circuit Q29BD, one of five 230-kv circuits connecting the generation of Beck to the Toronto-Hamilton load area."[16] Before examining these findings in further detail it is necessary to review some practices in the electrical industry. High-voltage transmission lines are subject to various natural hazards such as lightning, falling trees, and wind damage to the lines and towers. In the event of a lightning stroke, for example, the voltage of a line would suddenly rise to very high level causing an arc-over to ground around the insulators. This conducting path would continue to drain off the generated power unless the line were taken out of service momentarily. It would have to be isolated from the system, with other lines in parallel picking up its load, then switched back into service. To provide this protection, each leg of a transmission system is monitored by automatic devices that detect any abnormal conditions and take corrective action. These sensitive and fast-acting relays, in turn, operate the more massive and cumbersome circuit breakers that handle large amounts of power. It has been proposed in the past that magnetic fields accompanying UFOs induce current surges in the lines as they fly at high speed across the rights-of-way.[17] These surges would then be detected with the resulting isolation of the line. As a section of line is removed from service, the transfer of its power may cause an overload on a parallel line, and so on as the disturbance propagates throughout the whole system. These relays are the points at which trouble begins, and the previously quoted FPC report indicated that "The precise cause of the backup relay energization is not known." This admission was then followed by a discussion of some possible system conditions that could have triggered it.

The clues to some of these puzzles sometimes hide in the detailed sequence of the reported events. For this reason, an obscure power failure in Brazil takes on special significance. On August 17, 1959, the automatic keys at the Uberlandia power station suddenly disconnected power to all four trunks. A technician at a substation 45 miles away immediately telephoned to report that all the keys at his location had been automatically disconnected as a UFO passed overhead, traveling in the direction of the generating station along the lines. The chief engineer then manually reset the keys at the main station, but they all automatically turned off again. At that moment he ran outside and saw a bright object in the sky approaching at high speed, later calculated to be 1,500 mph. As soon as the UFO passed, the entire system returned to normal.[18] The critical point in this report is that operation of the relays at the substation occurred when the UFO was directly overhead. Those at the main station, clearly out of range of influence from the UFO, detected an abnormal condition and apparently responded properly. A two-stage mechanism for this interference would involve first the induction of a surge in the lines and then corrective action by the relay. Instead, it appears that the influence of the UFO was exerted directly upon the relay itself without any intervening process. Design details of these devices assure that they would be sensitive to stray radiation. The heart of the induction-type relay is a small, circular plate of metal with a spindle rigidly attached at the center. Bearings at the ends of the spindle permit free rotation, and under normal conditions, the metallic disc is held in stationary balance by a spring acting against electromagnetic forces that are derived from the conditions on the line being monitored.

In the event of an undesirable condition, rotation of the disc closes the contacts for taking corrective action. Clearly, high-frequency electromagnetic radiation from a UFO would induce eddy currents in the disc, disrupting its delicate balance and actuating a circuit breaker. Induction of stray currents could also operate a plunger-type relay that is in common use, essentially a solenoid like an electric door bell, although these devices should be more resistant to interference than the others. The possible effect upon a third type of relay utilizing solid state electronics is simply not known. Of course, the induced operation of the electromagnetic relays would cause no damage. "Ostensibly, backup relay #Q-29 at the Sir Adam Beck generating station, Queenston, Ontario, was eventually pinpointed as the source of the massive failure. But further investigation, hardly noted in the press, showed that nothing in the relay was broken when it was removed for inspection. In fact, it went back into operation automatically when power was restored. The line it was protecting was totally undamaged."[19] Induced operation of the protective relays by electromagnetic radiation from UFOs is probably the reason for these power blackouts.

The history of science has shown that it is the things that don't fit, the apparent exceptions to the rule, that signal potential break-throughs in our concept of the world about us.
— J. Allen Hyneck

CHAPTER 6

PHYSIOLOGICAL EFFECTS

Effects of UFOs upon the principal sensory organs have been explored elsewhere. It was found, in brief, that the visual experience involved images of metallic vehicles, including various structural details, which were sometimes surrounded by vivid displays in brilliant colors or dazzling halos. A study of their noises disclosed several distinct types and suggested the artificial stimulation of auditory sensations within the head. Finally, several unique odors noticed in the vicinity of UFOs were traced to specific chemical compounds that are formed in the atmosphere under the stimulus of radiant energy that is emitted by UFOs. Reception of signals by the eyes, ears, and nose have been accounted for, yet there remains a variety of ways in which the body responds to UFOs at short range.

Primary Symptoms

A sensation of body heating during a close encounter is a common complaint. A huge craft, 70 meters long, flew within 30 meters of two sheriffs in Texas causing a heat wave.[1] Six teenagers in Ohio experienced the same reaction as a disc-shaped machine hovered overhead.[2] The intensity of this effect is, of course, variable and it may reach frightful proportions. Near the Capitan Curbelo Naval Air Station in Uruguay an experienced pilot flew his light plane to within 700 meters of a brilliant object shaped like a "musical top" that had come to a dead stop directly ahead on his flight path. "I saw that (the UFO) rocked twice in a balancing motion. Then it took off in the direction of the sea at a fantastic speed. It left a little trail in the form of water vapor . . . . The temperature was greatly increased, so much that I had to open the windows and door of the plane, and take off my field jacket. I almost fainted."[3] A stronger heat wave in the cockpit of an F94 jet during a UFO chase became so unbearable that the pilot and his crewman had to bail out. The plane crashed in Walesville, New York, tragically killing four people and injuring others.[4] Actual burns of first and second degree, usually on the face and hands, have been the reward of unwary people who approached UFOs too closely or of others innocently minding their own business when one flew past at very close range.[5]

Sometimes the witnesses are temporarily paralyzed while the UFO is nearby, usually within 50 to 150 meters.[6] A farmer in San Pietro, Italy, became paralyzed when he approached to within 10 meters of a UFO that had landed in the village square.[7] Three figures moving around a landed UFO at Stratford-on-Avon held the attention of a man who could not move until they boarded the craft and flew away.[8] In at least seven other instances, witnesses were immobilized during the encounter, but their involuntary body functions, such as breathing, heart beat, and vision, were unimpaired.[9] Return to normalcy was usually immediate when the UFO left, but it took about 20 minutes for one victim to regain his muscular coordination.[10] Approximately the same amount of time was required by a French farmer to recover, although his paralysis was probably induced by some kind of a weapon.[11]

Loss of consciousness is also relatively frequent, being reported as either an isolated symptom or in association with other symptoms.[12] Quite significantly, about half of the people who were either paralyzed or who had lost consciousness also described feeling a prickling sensation or an electrical shock. As a man in Massachusetts explained, "My mind was not at all affected. I just could not move, felt like shock and numbness."[13]

Because of the prominent association between the other physiological effects and the feeling of electrical shock, one is inclined to ascribe the cause of the symptoms to some electrical phenomenon. That temptation becomes overwhelming when a tabulation of the cases reveals that, in nearly every instance of bodily heating, paralysis, loss of consciousness, or electrical shock, *automobile engines were also stopped or began to misfire.* In two instances, headlamps also went out.[14] This definite correlation between the effects upon the human body and upon electrical circuits clearly points to electromagnetic energy as the causative agent, a relationship that has long been suspected.[15] "Loud humming" and "beeping," whose origin was probably electromagnetic, were also heard just prior to paralysis and unconsciousness.[16] Obviously the sounds must precede or follow the loss of consciousness, since by definition, an unconscious person is oblivious to external stimuli. At any rate, the instant-by-instant sequence of events in these sightings should be examined with care. Painful pricklings like an electrical shock were felt by a motorist in France as his child, also riding in the car, began to cry. The pain increased, then the engine failed and the lights went out.[17] In other words, the electrical shock gradually increased up to the point that the responsible agent disrupted the electrical circuits of the car. Had the increase continued further, one suspects that the witness may have become paralyzed. While this instance stands alone, it does suggest that the prickling sensation is an early manifestation of the radiant energy, followed by electrical interference and, finally, paralysis or unconsciousness. Probably the most sensitive response to the radiation is auditory, for, it may be recalled, the Hills first heard a beeping sound and then felt the prickling sensation.[18] Both the physiological and physical responses seem to be related to a flight maneuver of the UFOs. In two cases, conditions were normal until the

UFOs began to rise at which time the lights of one car went out[19] and the engine of the other failed.[20] In still another case, pricklings and paralysis occurred at the same time that the engine slowed down when a nearby UFO rose off the ground.[21] The strength of the causative agent, known to be ineffective at great distance, seems to depend upon the proximity of the UFO and appears to be strongest when the UFOs apply a burst of power at take-off.

A considerable variety of other physiological effects have also been noted in isolated instances. These include amnesia, headache, eye pain, loss of vision, nausea, and vomiting. Specific instances of these ailments will be taken up after some insights are developed concerning the primary symptoms.

Several factors point directly toward microwave energy as being responsible for the physiological effects. Such energy is known to be radiated from UFOs. It is the primary candidate for disrupting electrical circuits, and the failure of headlights and engines correlates well with heating of the body, electrical shock, paralysis, and loss of consciousness, all of which are induced by UFOs from some distance. The search for an understanding of these physiological effects should begin with an examination of related physical and biological data. Further searching should not be required if the technology of microwaves and the life processes together reveal specific mechanicms that can duplicate the observations.

Heating

Diathermy is a medical process for applying heat to tissues deep within the human body. It is usually accomplished by placing the part to be treated between suitably contoured electrodes that are padded with towels. An alternating potential applied to the plates causes them to act as a condenser in which the human tissues are the dielectric. Alternating electrical fields between the plates, completely penetrating the treated part, agitate molecules in the tissue and generate the desired heat. An antenna, substituted for the plates at microwave frequencies, beams electromagnetic radiation into the patient with the same penetrative result. A commercial machine for microwave diathermy operates with an output power of 100 watts at 2,450 MHz.[22] The penetration is excellent at that frequency, although it diminishes at higher frequencies, tending to concentrate the absorbed energy into a shallow layer near the skin.[23] Some potential danger attends the use of microwaves on people because the human body has heat receptors only on the skin. Overheating, therefore, might occur in the deeper tissues without the forewarning of pain, especially in portions not cooled by freely flowing blood, as in bone marrow and the eyes. In the previous discussion of UFO plasmas, the gases were estimated to have temperatures in the range of roughly 200° to 400°F. Such hot gases will radiate energy over a wide spectrum that includes the infrared, visible, and ultraviolet. Heating of the skin and even serious burns could be produced by the infrared rays, depending upon their intensity and the duration of exposure. Typical sunburns could be produced by the ultraviolet rays. As both types of radiation are blocked by clothing, they would cause localized effects upon the bare skin of the face and hands. The more generalized experience of "heat waves" that force people to remove clothing and to jump out of airplanes must have a different origin. Absorption of high-frequency radiation with the generation of heat as in microwave diathermy, is a likely candidate.

Paralysis

Control of the human body is the task of the central nervous system. It receives information on the circumstances outside the body from the senses and status reports on internal conditions such as the muscular needs for oxygen. This data is incorporated into the general experience and conscious desires of the individual. Two major sets of signals are then sent out along nerves to the muscles and glands to implement a response that is appropriate to the conditions prevailing at that instant. This process is continuous. Of primary concern at present are the functional properties of nerve fibers. In some ways these fibers resemble insulated electrical wires. A central core of protoplasmic material, a moderately good conductor of electricity, is surrounded by a sheath of membrane of a fatty substance that is a moderately good insulator. Orders to outlying muscles, sent by the central nervous system, travel along these fibers as a wave of electrical potential. The similarity to electrical wires cannot be carried very far, however, fibers have certain unique properties. The traveling pulse, known as an action potential, always has the same intensity in a particular fiber. At any point along the fiber, it is either present or it is not; it never shows up only partially or at a potential above the norm. Energy for transmission of this signal derives from the fiber itself, not from some driving force at the input end. The sheath is interrupted at intervals of about 1 millimeter, called Ranvier nodes, and the transmission energy is supplied by the passage of certain ions through the membranes in these short segments. The width of the pulse is about 1 millisec and it travels at various speeds, depending upon the size of the fiber, typically on the order of 10 meters per second. Measurements of electrical potentials inside the sheath show that a fiber at rest is about 0.07 volts negative compared to the external solution. An action potential traveling down the fiber has a positive amplitude of about 0.10 to 0.12 volts. Therefore, at the moment the action potential occupies a position in the fiber, its interior experiences a momentary swing that is about 0.04 volts positive compared to the outside. Experimental electrodes implanted in the fiber at any location can trigger the standard pulse by impressing a potential difference across the membrane of about 0.02 volts or greater. Pulses then travel outward in both directions along the fiber, although they would normally travel in only one direction. After the pulse has been passed through one segment of the fiber, a finite time is required for that segment to return to normal. During the recovery period, it is completely incapable of transmitting another pulse. For about one millisecond the fiber cannot be stimulated at all; for roughly another millisecond it can, but only by a stimulus stronger than usual.[24] If a stimulus below the threshold of 0.02 volts is followed by another within about 2 millisec, then the second one may evoke a response even though it too is weaker than the threshold. The first stimulus opens the gate, so to speak, for the next ones.[25]

If microwave radiation were capable of providing the requisite stimulus, then an action potential would be induced. It has been found, in fact, that microwave radiation can create the necessary electrical tension across the membrane. By inserting miniature electrodes into nerve fibers, the potential difference between the inside and the outside can be measured. Irradiation by microwaves induces potentials that are typically in the millivolt range, but are sometimes as high as 0.10 volt, five times stronger than the threshold value of 0.02 volt.[26] As action potentials triggered by this mechanism would be identical in every respect to those that are sent out by the central nervous system, there would be no way in which the receptors could detect them to be frauds. Muscular response would be absolutely dictated by such artifically produced stimuli.

Traveling along a nerve at 10 meters per second, the pulse would progress a distance of 1 cm in 1 millisecond. As it takes about that long for the sheath to recover, the traveling pulse carries with it a zone of desensitized fiber about 1 cm in length, like the wake of a motorboat. The zone would actually be about twice that long since as the fibers gradually return to normal within about 1 millisecond after the first millisec period when they are absolutely refractive. Bear in mind that this dead zone does not remain stationary, but moves along the nerve immediately behind the action potential with the same speed.

Now consider the chain of events that would occur if a burst of microwave radiation should stimulate the nerve fiber at several locations. Action potentials would propagate away from the sites of origin in *both* directions. From neighboring sites, therefore, two pulses traveling toward one another must collide. Up to the instant of contact, the two pulses are being followed by their respective wakes of desensitized fiber. They cannot interpenetrate or continue traveling in their original directions because the dead zone of the other is not capable of furnishing the propagation. For the same reason, they cannot be reflected back along their course. Upon colliding, they must both be annihilated. The last indication of their existence would be the electrical change in the small segment where they met. Centered upon the site of their disappearance would be a section of the nerve about 2 cm long that would remain dormant for about 1 millisecond. Several such events happening at the same time would take a sizeable fraction of the nerve out of service momentarily. Should a second burst of microwave energy inundate the nerve while several sections are still dormant, more action potentials will be stimulated in those normal portions between the dormant zones that have recovered from the passage of the last pulse. Then the process leading to annihilation of contra-traveling pulses simply starts again. It is most interesting to explore the conditions that might be established in the nerve by microwave energy that is itself being pulsed about 500 times per second. First of all, the effective threshold for stimulation would be lowered by the "gate effect" and action potentials could be induced more readily. The individual bursts of microwave energy would arrive at intervals of 2 milliseconds, which is approximately the time that the dead zones persist at the points of annihilation. Action potentials would be stimulated only in the responsive sections, which immediately thereafter would become insensitive. Meanwhile, previously exhausted sections would recover and become active again, just in time to be stimulated by the next burst of microwaves. One can envision a state of quasi-equilibrium in which a chain of sections, alternately insensitive and responsive, are switching their roles approximately 500 times per second. At all times, about half the nerve would be completely incapable of transmitting any signal.

Next consider the fate of legitimate impulses issued by the brain. They would obviously get wiped out upon meeting artificially induced pulses that were traveling the wrong way. They would disappear in the annihilation process—a most efficient means of disposing of signals that were intended for control of the muscles. As shown before, a series of pulses cannot be closer together in the nerve than the length of the dead zone. This restriction establishes an absolute upper limit to the message-handling capacity of the nerve. For a nerve having a propagation speed of 10 meters per second, as was assumed for the previous discussion, the dead zone is about 1 cm long. Therefore, the absolute upper limit of signal density occurs when they are 1 cm apart. At their common velocity, they would pass a given point at the rate of one every millisecond, or 1,000 of them in 1 sec. But because the nerve membrane requires an additional amount of time to recover, the spacing will be about 2 cm and that figure would be cut in half. The maximum rate of propagation in this nerve is estimated to be roughly 500 pulses per second. The behavior of this fiber under a steady, prolonged stimulus should reveal the correct value. Consider an electrical potential greater than the threshold to be applied and maintained across the sheath. It would respond by initiating an action potential and would then enter its refractory period. As soon as it recovers, it again experiences the stimulus and responds, and so on. The rate at which the action potentials are triggered in this experiment is the maximum propagation rate for that nerve. It has been found in the laboratory that such a sustained stimulus causes the emission of a train of pulses, usually 4 or 5 with gradually increased spacing, in about 100 milliseconds.[27] Apparently the capacity of the sheath to continue at its maximum transmission rate is severely limited, a point which cannot be pursued further without access to the original laboratory reports. These findings are significant to the annihilation of the action potentials originating in the brain. Such pulses may have to travel as far as 1 meter to contract a leg muscle, a journey that would take about 0.1 sec. A microwave field pulsed very slowly would leave large gaps of time during which muscular coordination would be normal, although sporadic disruption would occur. Higher pulse rates would increase the difficulty of control. At frequencies equal to, or greater than the maximum rate that the signals can be sent through the nerve, pulses from the brain would have no chance of getting through.

At the muscle end of the motor nerve, impulses are delivered to the receptors at the maximum rate. A single impulse causes a muscle fiber to contract for a finite period, say, 0.01 sec. If another pulse arrives during that period, the muscle is again stimulated to contract before having an opportunity to relax. Hence, a rapid series of such pulses will hold the muscle in a state of sustained contraction. A difficulty arises here, however. All skeletal muscles occur in pair-sets. Any kind of bodily motion, which is governed by one set of muscles can be compensated by another motion governed by the opposite set. A volitional action is accomplished by contracting the appropriate set of muscles while inhibiting their counterparts, an enormously complex obligation of the central nervous system. As microwaves cannot make such distinctions, all the motor nerves are stimulated indiscriminately. The net result is obvious: sets of muscles contract in opposition to each other and the body freezes into rigid immobility.

A mechanism to explain the typical UFO paralysis thus emerges. A pulsed microwave field emitted by the UFO weakens the threshold and stimulates action potentials in the motor nerves. Half of these travel the wrong way and nullify the signals issued by the brain. The witness suddenly becomes paralyzed, in whatever position he held at the time, by a stream of fraudulent pulses causing the skeletal muscles to work against each other. When the field intensity falls too low, everything usually returns to normal. As an Australian youth said after two minutes in that condition, he was "merely cognizant of things as they were without being able to react."[28] The microwaves apparently stimulate only the nerves to the voluntary muscles without producing a comparable effect upon the nerves to the involuntary body functions, including muscles and glands. Sensory channels also seem to be immune from influence, except perhaps the auditory nerve. How the excitation process can be so selective is not at all clear. It is known that nerve fibers of small diameter have higher thresholds than larger ones.[29] Perhaps the answer is very simple—the larger nerves controlling voluntary actions are easier to stimulate. Because of health hazards, humans have not been exposed to high-intensity microwave fields, and there is no laboratory indication of a paralyzing effect.

Electrical Shock

As the power output of many large radars has increased enormously in the last two decades, some special precautions have been taken. Several costly installations were constructed to detect missiles over the horizon that might be launched toward the United States. This system provides about 15 minutes warning time for retaliatory action. Potential exposure of 20 times the allowable flux of microwave energy at these sites prohibits the performance of routine maintenance while the radars are in operation. As it is unthinkable to shut down periodically for any purpose, special protective clothing for the technicians had to be developed. These suits cover the entire body, head, face, hands and feet. They are made from a metallized nylon to reflect electromagnetic energy away from the wearer. A special design assures electrical continuity across the seams. As electrical fields of thousand of volts per meter were also predicated, the suits have an exterior insulating layer of neoprene-coated nylon.[30] This layer prevents surges of current through the conducting layer that would otherwise be produced if a workman touched two metal pipes having different electrical potentials. In an environment of this nature, but of lesser intensity, an unprotected worker or a UFO witness might well experience an electrical shock.

Because microwave fields induce currents in electrical conductors, the military forces must take further precautions. They must make sure that ordnance is not accidentally detonated by stray radiation. This problem is most severe where ordnance must be handled close to powerful radar sets. On Navy ships, for example, the operational use of radar might have to be restricted. Primary research on this problem is conducted by the Electromagnetic Hazards Division of the Naval Weapons Laboratory in Dahlgren, Virginia.[31] In view of the importance of radiation-induced currents in the military experience, one would certainly anticipate an electrical effect upon the human body while exposed to microwaves. As moist skin is a good conductor and well furnished with sensory receptors, a prickling sensation would be quite expectable.

Loss of Consciousness

One component of the central nervous system regulates such body functions as sleep, temperature, blood pressure, other autonomic functions, and the emotional states. The nature of this control mechanism is fundamentally chemical; that is, the organ controls the production of small amounts of powerful agents such as adrenaline and serotonin. Experiments in 1952 showed that electrical stimulation of the thalamus increased the production of serotonin.[32] A similar electrical stimulation induced by microwaves could have the same result, that is, production of sleep-inducing chemicals.

Secondary Symptoms

Among the less frequent but notable ailments following close exposure to UFOs is the common headache. Two UFOs that landed in Brazil discharged three small beings from one and two from the other. These beings stood around talking for about 5 minutes before conducting a thorough inspection of both craft. All the while, they were being watched by a 15-year-old boy, whose companions were up ahead of him en route to a movie. After the UFO took off, the boy suddenly suffered violent headaches. As standard medication gave no relief for 5 days, he was taken to a doctor by his father.[33] In another situation, a bright disc-shaped craft, producing a high-pitched sound, came down near Rio de Janeiro and hovered, while three of its occupants walked nearby. One of the witnesses later suffered severe headaches.[34] Not only are the headaches clearly associated with the sightings, but in these two cases, the headaches began *after* the UFOs had left, a most puzzling detail. Whether the radiation received during the observation had anything to do with this symptom is doubtful, but it should be noted for the record that headaches are sometimes produced by microwaves. A study was conducted in 1943 involving 45 men with histories of exposure to low levels of microwave radiation spanning periods of 2 months to 9 years. "Several of these men reported frontal headaches and a flushed heating sensation when standing within 3 ft of a generating antenna."[35] The abbreviated source material unfortunately does not indicate the strength of the beam or whether the subjects were exposed directly to it. Also, these histories of exposure to microwaves are not typical of UFO witnesses. But the important aspect is that headaches were experienced and, apparently, only while the subjects were being irradiated. Because of the gross disparity in the time factors here, the cause for headaches associated with UFOs is lacking an explanation.

On rare occasions, the witnesses describe a loss of vision, either total or partial, resulting in cloudy or hazy images. A typical example involved a 37-year-old man in Pennsylvania who saw a large disc fly in front of the moon. Twenty minutes later both eyes became pained and his vision hazy. He gradually lost vision in both eyes; within several days, it returned to normal. His entire body was "sunburned." A doctor who examined him attributed the effects to ultraviolet exposure.[36] That diagnosis may well be correct, since unique blue light on or about the UFO was reportedly very intense for about 3 seconds at the end of the sighting. Consider, however, the oddity that the skin irritation was not confined to exposed portions of the body. As the witness had just put his car in the garage, according to the report, it may be presumed that he was normally attired. His clothing should have protected most of the body, since ultraviolet rays are easily stopped by a cotton shirt. Whatever troubled his eyes also penetrated his clothing. Recall that the propulsion system of UFOs involves the emission of microwave energy that, on occasion, excites the xenon molecules in the atmosphere to emit their characteristic bright blue. Microwaves pass through clothing without significant loss, but at frequencies used in diathermy they also penetrate deeply into the human body. At somewhat higher frequencies, above 3,000 MHz, tissue penetration is greatly abated and nearly half of the impinging energy is absorbed on the skin. Absorption of microwave energy in the skin produces conditions that are indistinguishable from ordinary sunburn arising from an excess of ultraviolet rays. In all probability, this witness suffered a flash burn on the retina and "sunburn" over his entire body by a 3-second exposure to microwaves at a frequency greater than 3,000 MHz.

The eyes are especially sensitive to microwaves, whose energy is readily absorbed by the internal fluid, the aqueous humor. In addition, when wavelengths of the radiation are approximately the same dimension as the eyeball the conditions for a tuned cavity prevail in which absorption is further enhanced. Absorbed energy raises the eye temperature, a very dangerous condition even for small increases that cannot be felt. As the lens is very intolerant of stress, the abnormal temperature can generate cataracts. Furthermore, microwaves produce a direct effect upon the lens involving chemical changes resulting in the formation of cataracts.[37] For these reasons, the allowable exposure to the eyes is severely limited and eye protection is a must. Cataracts produced by microwaves do not normally progress to total blindness, and they gradually disappear. That such lenticular opacity, or cloudiness of the aqueous humor, has been induced by UFOs seems fairly clear. A doctor examining one witness with hazy vision "could not see the retina," presumably because of opacity of the lens or eye fluid.[38]

After stopping the car of an Australian businessman, a mushroom-shaped UFO aimed a strong beam of light toward him. He later found himself driving down the road, unable to remember starting the car.[39] He had suffered amnesia covering a brief span of time, and the reported beam of light indicates a purposeful act by the UFO occupants. In a previous chapter, review of two other instances of memory lapse showed deliberate action also. Amnesia, however, appears to be rare and not merely a consequence of being too close to a UFO.

Sighting a UFO is sometimes quite a shock to the witness. Anything so completely out of the ordinary could overwhelm a person's effort to adjust to his surroundings. The most sturdy personality might have some difficulty, and the experience could prove to be too stunning for an individual whose struggle with life has left little reserve strength. In order to escape from the anxiety of the situation, some witnesses may subconsciously respond hysterically, they may experience unusual sensations of vision, hearing, taste, or smell, their body might suddenly go rigid for a moment, waves of nausea could trouble them for days; or their subsequent behavior patterns may be completely out of character. These reactions to stress, being of purely psychological origin, can obviously mimic some of the physiological responses that have been described above. It would be moderately easy to confuse some of the emotional and physiological effects. The error in either direction would be serious, namely, falsely ascribing a physiological cause to a purely emotional reaction, or inadvertently overlooking a valid physiological explanation. Some protection against the latter pitfall is afforded by automobile engines and radios that are not inclined to be neurotic. Their malfunctions require a specific, physical agency. When that agency is identified and it produces a physiological response in the witness, a psychological explanation is not required and, indeed, is superfluous.

Scientific Uncertainty

In the face of substantial evidence to the contrary, most American researchers cling to the notion that absorption of microwaves in the human body produces nothing but heat. Varied biological changes, they contend, are traceable to a rise in temperature. The concept of a direct biochemical effect is rejected with several arguments. The radiation dosage, for example, cannot be reliably reported because there are no generally accepted standards of instrumentation. Or, perhaps, the possibility of a purely thermal response in the tissues has not been disproven. A recent review article points out that "There are many areas in which presently available data are questionable, contradictory, or inapplicable."[40] Microwave research in the United States certainly suffers more confusion than becomes a scientific discipline. On the international scene, the situation is no better. A summary of Soviet views indicates, among other things contradicting the American position, that "At the present time, the opinion of most Soviet investigators is that microwaves: . . . affect the structure and chemical reactivity of neutral cells."[41] Russian research purports to demonstrate sub-threshold effects, that is, irreversible chemical changes that are produced at levels below the onset of any thermal responses. Furthermore, these changes are believed to be cumulative. Without ever being exposed to levels of radiation causing damage by heat, according to these views, a worker exposed repeatedly to low-level microwaves at his job might suffer serious injury over a period of time. These beliefs are reflected in the safety standards that have been adopted; permissible limits of exposure in Russia are 1,000 times more conservative than in the United States.[42] This disparity persists because the methods, rationale, and data of the Soviet scientists appear to be obscure and nebulous to the Americans. At any rate, most of the symptoms produced by UFOs, being inadmissible to American science, are thoroughly compatible with the Russian findings.

One Russian conclusion that is especially vague to Americans is the alleged "asthenia" syndrome, a combination of mental and personality changes. "The symptoms include weakness, fatigability, depression, antisocial tendencies, sense of fear, impairment of memory and general mental function and an inability to make decisions."[43] During the '60s the U.S. Embassy in Moscow was reportedly found to be permeated by abnormal levels of microwave radiation, presumably beamed there to confuse the diplomats and make them more tractable in negotiations. Subsequent experiments on monkeys in the U.S. by the Advanced Research Projects Agency yielded no definite conclusions on the matter. The Russians may have had this type of plan in mind during the international chess tournament, when the American, Bobby Fischer, was accused of using "electronic devices and chemical substances" to gain an unfair advantage. Concerning the Russian Spassky, his assistant commented that ". . . it is the first time that I observe such unusual slackening of concentration and display of impulsiveness in his playing . . ." A thorough search disclosed no incriminating evidence.

Observers Reactions

Witnesses, who have been exposed to microwave radiation from UFOs should be good candidates for displaying symptoms of the asthenia syndrome propounded by the Russians. An artificial sense of fear, for example, might be experienced when that emotion was inappropriate, or in intensities not warranted by the circumstances. For the most part, distant observations of UFOs are accompanied by entirely normal behavior. Relatives and neighbors are called out of their houses to verify the experience. Police officers and pilots contact others on their radio networks for the same purpose. A motorist may stop to watch the show or drive to another location for an unobstructed view. These patterns would be expected in events that are sometimes so distracting that witnesses forget to use their cameras. Responses at closer range vary greatly, but a few patterns can be discerned. Upon spotting a disc-shaped machine descend and come to rest on its landing gear, a witness might rush toward it for a closer examination, especially when he later affirms that the incident was entirely beyond anything else in his experience. Such behavior, however, is rare. A few people have moved in for a closer look,[44] even to the point of standing immediately adjacent to the UFOs and touching them.[45] More typical, however, is a negative reaction in which the witness takes refuge in hiding, runs away from the scene, or if in a car, drives away in reckless disregard for traffic laws. People seem to be genuinely afraid of UFOs, but they may only be unnerved by rainbow colors cascading off their edges or by some other oddity. The imminent landing of a large wheel with flaming openings in front sent two Brazilian workers into hiding.[46] Two youngsters ran for cover from an object circling overhead that resembled an up-side-down plate.[47] Two British airmen remained unperturbed while watching a dome-shaped object land behind a hangar, but took to their heels when an opening appeared in the UFO.[48] Two young New Zealanders also held their ground in the presence of a UFO until a similar opening made them think that it was about to land.[49] Three hunters, a breed not easily frightened, ran away from a very large, egg-shaped object that they discovered hovering in a Venezuelan forest.[50] Of course, stronger emotional impact has occurred. A large sphere of orange light so frightened a 16-year-old boy in Indiana that he lost control of his bicycle.[51] A low-flying object terrified two witnesses in Georgia, who abandoned their bicycles and ran home nearly hysterical.[52] An Italian was paralyzed with fear by a metallic object, 10 meters in diameter, hovering close to the ground.[53] As seen in previous sections, however, this last witness may have been paralyzed for physiological, rather than emotional, reasons.

It is necessary here to anticipate the subject matter of two later chapters by summarizing the reactions of witnesses upon confronting strange occupants of UFOs. Unadulterated, bone-rattling fear seems to be found exclusively in this context. Four Canadian children were panic stricken by an extremely tall UFO pilot who held out his hand to them saying something that was unintelligible.[54] A dark figure the size of a man, with wings like a bat, thoroughly spooked some British teenagers.[55] A creature emerging from a UFO in Gabon terrified a fisherman who was watching from nearby.[56] Some small creatures attacking three Argentine students enroute to school threw them into a state of terror.[57] Several adults and children in Peru panicked at the sight of a very small creature walking the street leaving a luminous trail.[58] And so on.[59] It is perfectly normal for people to flee in terror from strange beings, particularly when the people are young, as is most often the case, and when the creatures act in a threatening manner, or actually attack.

While these data carry a modest load of ambiguity, they do not generally sustain the Russian concepts. The level of fear displayed during the encounters with UFOs and their occupants seems to be within normal bounds, although rather high at times. It must be mentioned that the Russian research pertains to repeated exposures to low-level radiation whereas these examples do not.

Unfortunately, this issue cannot be put to rest so neatly, for other sources of information tend to support the opposite conclusion, namely, that abnormal feelings of fear are induced in the witnesses by UFOs at close range. In a series of sightings in New Hampshire, nearly all the witnesses were very frightened. The investigator of these incidents observed that ". . . some people were in actual shock or hysteria as a result of extremely low-level encounters with the objects."[60] Descriptive terms used by the witnesses emphatically showed their reactions to be very intense and, under the circumstances, probably inappropriate. Despite the absence of any recognized threat to life or limb, witnesses were variously reported to be badly shaken or scared to death.[61] Emotional experiences, described on two occasions as "shivery feeling" and "funniest feeling through me," may have been artifical or merely the natural accessory to fear. An interesting suggestion of a direct influence by a UFO occurred when a witness panicked while within close range, drove away to report the sighting to the police, and upon regaining composure, returned to the scene for a second look. While these reports are inconclusive on this point, they require that the question of UFO-induced emotional states remain open. It is hoped that further insight may be achieved from independent studies in the future and from the analysis of animal behavior in the following section.

Animals Too

As the higher animals are physiologically very similar to man, a close parallel is expected between their reactions to UFOs and those of people. Any marked differences would be a clue that beckons for further research into the causes. Source materials for this section are some 200 animal incidents compiled by a British quarterly.[62]

Millions of delicate UFO detectors are already distributed in a world-wide network. Each one is carefully maintained in top condition and monitored round the clock for any response signifying the presence of a UFO. Man's best friend is also his best UFO detector. Very commonly, indeed, the first indication that a UFO is present or approaching is the excited barking of a dog or a whole neighborhood full. Suppose that some random noise sets a dog to barking; others within earshot may take up the call, and presently the whole neighborhood echoes with their racket. This kind of domino effect could be the basis for the area-wide disturbances of dogs near UFOs, although it doesn't seem likely. It is not an ordinary bark that is evoked by UFOs. In the language of the reports, one pooch was howling enough to awaken the dead,[63] one barked furiously, frothing at the mouth,[64] one carried on something terrible,[65] and one made a dreadful noise.[66] These animals were disturbed in some unique way; they were not just relaying the neighborhood gossip. Because dogs can sense the approach of UFOs before humans, one wonders if the detection is based upon keener hearing, as with the early announcement of an approaching police siren, or if another mechanism is responsible. Dogs dislike UFOS. In fact, they are terrified by them and seek to escape from them. Under circumstances clearly indicating a landed UFO was nearby, a Canadian woman heard knocks at her door. Her dog rushed forward, then suddenly retreated, trembling as if terrified, and retired into a corner.[67] When a man opened a door to investigate the cause of his dog's howling outside, the animal crawled in on its belly in abject terror. The man found a UFO and its pilots outside.[68] One of several dogs owned by a witness was so terrified that it ran into a barbed wire fence; the others whined while cowering on the ground.[69] A dog became disturbed in a car when a UFO was first sighted. By the time the driver was flagged down on the highway by the UFO people, the dog was lying in a tight ball under the seat, trembling violently.

He was still cowering there two hours later.[70] These animals exhibited symptoms of extreme fright. In some of these cases the animals could not see the UFOs. They had never read any science fiction nor been instructed how to act in the presence of a UFO. In other words, their behavior must have been induced by the UFOs. One must face the probability that their response was stimulated by microwaves, namely, a symptom of the asthenia syndrome as reported by Russian scientists. It should be most interesting to discover in the future why this response is seen more clearly in dogs than in people. If microwave radiation were inducing this sense of fear in the dogs, one would expect that a higher intensity might even paralyze them. A Frenchman out hunting with his dog saw two people climbing out of a small UFO on the ground, 40 meters away. He fled, but his dog, running toward the UFO, soon retreated, walking as though he were partially paralzed.[71] Perhaps the dog didn't get close enough to become completely paralyzed. An incident which occurred during the evening of October 21, 1963, in Trancas, Argentina is especially significant:

> Three very fierce dogs inside the house, and two dozen fowls outside, were for forty minutes cowed and paralyzed by a vivid hot beam of light, varying in colour from red to violet, directed at the house from one of a number of UFOs nearby. As the revolving beam returned and caught the dogs through the windows, they became apathetic and silent, recovering slightly in the intervals.[72]

Both a man and his dog were temporarily paralysed, at the same time, when an object dived down toward them and then climbed back into the sky.[73] It was luminous and white, a condition seen previously to coincide with the strongest emission of microwaves. In this case, the man and the dog were about equally susceptible to the induced paralysis. While there is no laboratory evidence of microwave paralysis in humans, experiments on small animals have produced motor paralysis that disappeared when the exposure was terminated.[74]

Physiological effects among animals are by no means limited

to dogs. Among the 200 cases under study, influences were also noted upon wild birds, pigeons, ducks, geese, chickens, turkeys, sheep, cows, horses, and cats. All these creatures are severely agitated by UFOs and they seem to fear them. A cat, hissing and spitting, leaped into the air and then hid under a bed,[75] sheep stampeded,[76] cows in the field panicked and ran away,[77] horses reared up and cattle did everything but turn somersaults,[78] and so on. Some of them may have been paralysed. With a whistling sound, a UFO landed in a meadow in Denmark. The witness became paralyzed when he approached within 50 meters and observed that nearby cows seemed unable to move. He further noted that birds had stopped singing.[79] Any naturalist knows that a disturbance in the woods causes birds to stop singing, and other wild creatures depend upon that change as an alarm signal. But the notion that the birds stopped singing because they had been paralyzed was also a prominent aspect of a sighting by three men in Brazil who were hunting crocodiles one night. A UFO on the opposite bank of a river caused an "awful, uncanny silence" to descend upon the forest. Not even a cicada was to be heard.[80] Not only were the usually noisy, tropical birds put out of action, but, perhaps, so were the insects.

A UFO was spotted one night standing on three legs on some railroad tracks 300 meters from a man's home. It rose silently while a dome on top started to spin and the legs retracted. It was gone in 20 seconds. The next day, the witness inspected the site with his dog. There were no marks or traces, but one sniff sent the dog dashing away, howling.[81] Things should return to normal immediately after a UFO has flown away, but unfortunately, they don't. Presumably the dog had no prior knowledge that he was visiting the site of a UFO landing, yet something disturbed him. Direct radiation from the UFO must be ruled out and another cause for his delayed reaction found. The language of the report itself provides the best clue that an odor was responsible. In a previous section concerning that subject, various noxious gases were found to be produced by UFOs. Some of these gases, being relatively heavy, could settle to the ground and linger for many hours.

A thick, gray disc coming straight down over a farm in Australia threw all the animals into a panic. For several days the cows could not be herded into the paddock over which the UFO had hovered.[82] A similar aversion was demonstrated by some cattle in Iowa. In the middle of the night, a cigar-shaped object remained on the ground for 20 minutes amidst a vivid, red illumination, crackling noises, and the odor of ozone. In the morning the cattle were found to have bolted to the end of the pasture, from where they refused to budge toward the landing site for feeding.[83] Fine strands resembling spider webs, known as angel hair, are sometimes discharged from UFOs for no apparent reason. This substance evaporates when touched and it has not been chemically analyzed.[84] Such material, falling into a field in Tennessee, caused the witnesses to become nauseated and to feel itching sensations. The same effects were experienced by everyone who entered the area during the next few days. During that period, the family dog would not leave the house nor would the cows be coaxed back to the site. Everything eventually returned to normal when rainfall apparently washed away the offensive substance.[85] Another possible source of offense to the animals is an odd, oily substance that is sometimes found at landing sites.[86] If some of this material could be retrieved from a future landing, and if its chemical composition should prove to be unique, animal reactions to it could produce some interesting case studies. A sample of such substance, having a purple color and the odor of 3-in-1 oil, was turned over to the authorities in 1965. Its composition was never published.[87]

In summary, dogs, being sensitive to the approach of UFOs, constitute a universal detection network. They display symptoms of extreme fear when the UFO is moderately close, even though they may be indoors or inside an automobile where they cannot see it. An artificial state of fear that is induced by radiation is the suspected cause of this reaction. Many domestic animals and perhaps some wild ones panic at the approach of a UFO. The radiation that at greater intensity apparently causes a biochemical psychosis, also paralyzes dogs, cows, probably birds, and possibly insects.

What constitutes proof?
        — Edward J. Ruppelt

CHAPTER 7

FLIGHT AND PROPULSION

UFOs have unusual and distinctive flight characteristics. This aspect of the subject has been investigated extensively for many years, usually with an emphasis upon documentation. Numerous cases have been cited to illustrate each feature of UFO flight.[1] Let it suffice here to consider a composite, hypothetical sighting that includes the prominent flight patterns so that the maximum space can be devoted to analysis.

A HYPOTHETICAL SIGHTING

During a midafternoon on a clear day, John Doe saw a silvery disc in the sky traveling with an undulating motion at an altitude he estimated to be 10,000 ft. Even though going four times faster than a jet, no sound was heard. After several abrupt changes in direction, it stopped suddenly, remaining stationary for about 10 minutes, except for a slight wobble on its axis. It next came down toward the witness to an altitude of about 100 ft from where it descended like a falling leaf to hover about 1 meter above the ground. When approached by the witness, it rose slowly to the level of the treetops, then zoomed out of sight with fantastic speed. John Doe said that he had never seen anything like it in his life.

Hovering

A favorite posture of UFOs is to hang nearly motionless in the sky or at very low altitude without any indication of how this stunt is achieved. Obviously, the objects do not depend upon aerodynamic lift as do conventional, fixed-wing aircraft. Neither are they suspended from large, rotating blades like helicopters. The absence of blasts of air or billows of smoke rules out jet engines and rockets. Nearly every investigator has the impression that UFOs are somehow defeating gravity, and obviously, they are.

A simple, scientific fact can be of help here. A hovering UFO does not defeat gravity entirely. If it did, it would not hover; instead, it would float upward in the atmosphere. Consider an idealized, disc-shaped UFO that is 10 meters in diameter and 2 meters thick, having a volume of 5,540 cubic feet and weighing 30 tons. On a calm day, no lateral forces are required to maintain its horizontal position. The UFO balances in the air vertically between a buoyant force upward, equal to the weight of air it displaces, and an equal force downward, presumably furnished by gravity. The magnitude of the buoyant force, amounting to the volume of the UFO times the density of displaced air, is easily calculated to be about 425 pounds weight at sea level. In other words, a downward force of about 425 lbs is required to prevent the UFO from rising. A hovering UFO, therefore, defeats gravity almost, but not quite, completely. In this example, the reduction in effective weight and mass is about 99.3%.

Descent and Ascent

One can best appreciate the problem of descent from the pilot's point of view. After bringing the craft to a dead stop about 50 ft above the selected landing spot, he must next lose altitude. Recall that he has just achieved a delicate balance of vertical forces. The descent could be accomplished by adjusting this balance to allow a stronger reaction with gravity. But it is doubtful that this method would be wise, because completing the maneuver would be unnecessarily complicated and possibly hazardous. Upon approaching the ground, it would not be adequate merely to return the control to its former position, since the vehicle would still be in motion downward. The control setting would first have to be reversed sharply to act as a brake then, upon stopping the downward motion, reset to the original position. If the pilot wished to complete the descent close to the ground, within 1 meter or less as is commonly observed, he would be in danger of overshooting the mark and crashing. A safer control method would be much preferred.

At the beginning of descent, a force from the hovering UFO is acting vertically upward to counteract the weight acting downward. Without modifying this lifting force, the pilot could simply tilt the craft slightly to one side by a small amount, say, the angle A. The force holding the craft in the air would then point in a direction making an angle A with the vertical, but the effective weight would continue to act straight down. The consequences of this arrangement are twofold. Firstly, a force would gradually build up to the small value of F sin A and push the craft gently in the direction of the tilt. Secondly, the force holding the craft in the air would be gradually reduced to the value of F cos A, being only slightly less than the original value. Subject to these forces, therefore, the craft would sink slowly as it moved sideways in the direction of tilt. The control lever would be brought back quickly to neutral. This maneuver would then be repeated on the opposite side, with additional loss of altitude accompanying a lateral slip in the new direction. By continuing this sequence, first to one side then to the other, the craft could be brought down to the desired altitude under perfect control until the control lever was left in its neutral position. There would be no hazard of overshoot, since the original, balanced forces were never changed. The common manner of UFO descent, called "falling leaf" or "pendulum," seems to be entirely explicable as a preferred method of control.

Again from the perspective of the pilot, consider how best to take off in a craft that is a virtual bomb, that is, capable of fantastic performance. There is obviously no hazard of overshooting in ascent, but the pilot must be mindful of obstructions such as trees, telephone lines, and buildings. As the control system used in descent is of no value whatever in ascent, the pilot must adjust the balance of forces on his craft. Recall that the idealized craft above had an effective weight of 425 lbs while hovering. By further defeating gravity and reducing this weight, the pilot can allow the buoyant force to dominate, causing the craft to rise gently as it floats upward in the atmosphere. Upon reaching a safe altitude, the pilot is free to fly to his next destination. Almost every observed departure of landed UFOs includes this two-stage maneuver, namely, a cautious rise of 50 to 100 ft followed by a spectacular blast-off. A case in point involved an Australian postmaster and a mail carrier who together watched a dome-shaped object in a field for 10 minutes before approaching to within 200 meters. The object then rose, hovered, and shot off at immense speed.[2]

Acceleration and Relativity

One of the most prominent but puzzling features of UFOs is their ability to change speed and direction of flight much more quickly than is possible for an airplane. Instead of making long, sweeping curves as a jetliner is compelled to do, they make sudden, nearly right-angle turns. Their general flight pattern is erratic or jerky, resembling the flight of hummingbirds, that dart hither and yon, hover temporarily, suddenly change altitude, and then zoom out of sight with astonishing swiftness. This manner may be not only characteristic of UFOs but essential to their mode of flight. At any rate, something very fundamental is suggested by it.

By technical analysis, it has been ostensibly shown that the lift-off of a UFO would require as much energy as the detonation of an atomic bomb, with accompanying temperatures of 85,000°C and intense deposits of radioactivity. As neither of these conditions prevails, the conclusion was drawn that UFOs could not be spacecraft controlled by extraterrestrial beings, because they did not obey the laws of physics. One further aspect was also explored:

> Let us now consider the possibility that the laws of physics are not valid. One idea frequently suggested is that extraterrestrial beings have discovered gravity shields. This, however, would not solve the problem of propulsion because inertia would remain; reaction would still be needed to obtain acceleration.[3,=]

Of course, the fundamental problem in understanding UFOs is that their peculiar flight pattern involves enormous accelerations for which adequate forces are not in evidence. The resolution of this dilemma appears to lie in the physical property of inertia.

If the UFO pilots are extra-terrestrial, and extra-intelligent as nearly everyone supposes, then they must certainly be familiar with the Theory of Relativity. By some semantic accident, this mathematical description of nature is still referred to as a "theory," whereas all the weaker descriptions that it has supplanted are known as "laws of nature." Relativity has become indispensable to every branch of the physical sciences, and its basic truth is verified daily in the operation of cyclotrons and linear accelerators, nuclear reactors in submarines, surface ships, and central power stations, and thankfully only on occasion, in the explosion of nuclear weapons. As the mathematical cornerstone for describing gravitational fields in astronomy and cosmology, it is consistent with all observations to date.[5] Of all the theories in the physical sciences, none is more trustworthy. With this major advance over Newtonian mechanics, Einstein recognized the inseparable relationship between gravitation and inertia, and "transformed the general principle of relativity from an epistemological postulate into a law of exact science."[6] According to the Principle of Equivalence, enunciated by Einstein, it is not possible to distinguish inertial forces from gravitational forces. In layman's language,

The validity of this principle will be evident to any aviator; for in an airplane it is impossible to separate the effects of inertia from those of gravitation. The physical sensation of pulling out of a dive is exactly the same as that produced by executing a steeply banked turn at high speed.[7]

To put this point in another perspective, inertial mass and gravitational mass cannot be distinguished; the property of matter that reacts to accelerations is the same as that which responds to gravitational fields. This identity is evidenced by two objects of different mass that, being otherwise identical, fall at the same rate when released in a gravitational field. The most recent experiments have established this fact to the extraordinary accuracy of 1 part in 10^{12}.[8] One may be quite assured in reckoning that gravitational mass and inertial mass are identical. Now to the bearing of these matters upon UFOs. *If, as has been suggested, UFOs nullify the effect of gravity upon their mass, it must follow that they will nullify their inertial behavior also*. Perhaps reference to a "gravity shield" is unfortunate because it presupposes a method which is not known. Nevertheless, a "gravity shield" must also function as an "inertial shield."

Consider a UFO having a certain mass while resting on its landing gear. By activating its so-called "shield," it reduces its effective mass respecting gravity to a very small fraction of its former value, permitting neutral buoyancy in the atmosphere, or to even lesser values approaching arbitrarily close to zero. What kind of performance could be expected from such a virtually massless vehicle? Very modest forces exerted upon it would produce extremely high accelerations. It could easily zoom out of sight in seconds as is often reported. Or it could accelerate so fast that the human eye could not follow, creating the illusion that it had disappeared instantly, like "turning off a light," or that it had slipped through a crack in some ill-conceived, special dimension. The eye cannot follow objects accelerating faster than about 20g, that is, 20 times earth's gravity. In the sixties, a popular toy was a multi-stage, plastic rocket powered by water from the garden hose and by entrapped air at the prevailing hydrant pressure. It was impossible to observe the departure of the second stage when it fired at about 20g. Similarly, the squashed appearance of a tennis ball against a racket and its initial rebound can be detected only with high-speed photography. While the ultimate truth on this topic may be far beyond the present level of comprehension, one need not appeal to the occult and mystical to explain the sudden disappearance of UFOs. By applying a suitable and possibly small force in the direction of flight, a "shielded" UFO of small effective mass could be brought to a very abrupt stop. Applying the force transversely would produce astonishingly sharp, nearly right-angle turns. Never mind the poor blokes inside—they would also be protected—by the "inertial shield."

The flight patterns so typical of UFOs are thoroughly consistent with, and even demand, a great reduction of their inertial, mass. And these characteristics occur in conjunction with a corresponding reduction of their response to gravity. One must conclude that the full range of UFO performance is internally consistent and in complete accord with General Relativity, which teaches that inertial mass and gravitational mass are exactly the same thing. This finding is all the more remarkable since few, if any, of the witnesses were theoretical physicists.

Undulation

Even in horizontal flight, UFOs display an odd habit that nags the rational mind, namely, bobbing up and down in a sinusoidal path. In the previous discussion on hovering it became clear that the true weight of a UFO at rest on the ground is greatly reduced while in flight, and it is along this line of reasoning that some progress may be made. First consider a UFO hovering at an altitude comparable to that of commercial jet traffic, say, 10 kilometers. The forces acting upon it must be in balance, as at sea level. But at this point another variable has been introduced: its altitude and corresponding atmospheric pressure. Since the atmosphere is more rarified at higher altitudes, the weight of a given volume of air is substantially less at high altitude than at sea level. Referring to the previous example, a volume of air weighing 425 lbs at sea level would weigh about 146 lbs at 10 kilometers, or only 32 lbs at 20 kilometers. Consequently, a UFO in buoyant equilibrium with the atmosphere at some altitude must have an effective weight substantially less than when hovering at sea level. The curious and somewhat startling implication here is that the extent to which a UFO defeats gravity must be dependent upon its altitude. Furthermore, by diminishing its effective mass to balance the reduced force of buoyancy at high altitude, the UFO cannot escape a parallel reduction in its mass insofar as inertial forces are concerned. It must be concluded that the inertial mass of a UFO diminishes with its altitude, approaching zero toward the limits of the earth's atmosphere, where buoyant forces are no longer significant. Flight characteristics that betray the lack of mass should be progressively more pronounced at high altitudes. It is especially significant to discover that the effective mass of UFOs may become vanishingly small, since the forces required to propel them through space under these conditions may be extremely small. This realization demands a thorough investigation of all possible means of propulsion, even though the forces available from them would appear, under ordinary circumstances, to be much too weak.

Now consider a UFO in horizontal flight with its effective mass being very small, depending upon the altitude. All the vertical forces are in balance, with gravity acting downward upon the effective mass. If the UFO should fly over a local area in which the strength of gravity were somewhat greater, it would temporarily experience an increase in the downward force. It would naturally respond by a displacement downward, a slight loss of altitude. Conversely, it would move slightly upward in passing over a zone of relatively weak gravity. The gravitational strength near the surface of the earth is nearly constant. It is slightly less at sea than on the continents, and the earth's rotation causes a small change that is dependent upon latitude; for example, the value of the acceleration of gravity at Fort Egbert, Alaska, is 982.183 cm/secs², compared to 978.331 cm/secs², at Bahia, Brazil.[9] Superimposed upon these global scale variations, however, are minor, local changes reflecting the density of underlying, geological structures, a fact that has been successfully exploited in geophysical prospecting. While these local changes are very small, usually less than 0.3%, they are probably strong enough to modify the flight path of a passing UFO and to produce the bobbing effect.

An alternative explanation for the undulatory motion has been implied in rare instances where the witness thought that the UFO was following the profile of the terrain, that is, maintaining a constant altitude above the ground in hilly country. An automatic control system based upon the reflection of radar-like signals from the ground would be capable of such performance and would be a considerable convenience to a busy pilot.

Speed and Shock Waves

A pilot and co-pilot for Mohawk Airlines spotted an interesting UFO one summer day in 1955 while cruising in their DC-3 at 3,000 ft near Utica, New York. An object passed at "great speed" 500 ft above their airplane. It was 150 ft wide, "light gray, almost round, with a center line . . ." At least four windows were observed emitting a bright blue-green light which seemed to change color as the object receded. It was also observed from two other aircraft. In addition, it was seen traveling east on airway Victor-2 from the control tower at Albany and by radar at Boston. Based upon the travel time between Utica and Boston, it must have been flying between 4,500 and 4,800 mph. And even at that speed, it did not produce a sonic boom. This sighting was not considered by the University of Colorado researchers to be due to anamalous propagation of radar signals; it was thought that it "must certainly be classed as an unknown pending further study, which it certainly deserves" but didn't get.[10] The literature abounds with examples of UFOs flying at unusually high speeds and, as in this example, being tracked on radar. Many of them were measured at speeds greater than the world record for airplanes at the time. And some substantially out-performed even experimental, rocket-powered aircraft, as was shown in an analysis of 81 radar cases, spanning the period 1941 through 1962.[11] In 1952, for example, the highest speed was about 1,200 mph, whereas in August of that year a UFO was tracked by an Air Defense Command radar at 4,000 mph. During a famous display over Washington, D.C., the previous month, radars operated both by the Air Force and the CAA tracked UFOs "on the order of 7500 mph," and some of these events were coordinated with visual sightings. Four months later, several objects over the Gulf of Mexico were tracked on radar aboard a B-29 in bursts of speed between 5,240 and 9,000 mph at an altitude of 18,000 ft.

With the development of large rockets in the space program, man has achieved speeds of about 18,000 mph while orbiting earth above the atmosphere, and naturally the UFOs have followed right along. This problem has been officially studied, and among a large number of sightings by astronauts all but three objects were ostensibly explained. A daytime observation of an object having angular extension and protrusions was especially puzzling.[12] In November 1969, American astronauts were reported on television to be followed by a strange object enroute to the moon while their booster was 4,000 miles away.[13] Considerable evidence suggests that observation of UFOs within the space program has been more frequent and significant than has been officially acknowledged.[14] At any rate, UFOs are clearly capable of speeds in the atmosphere far in excess of jets and rocket-powered airplanes.

When ordinary aircraft fly at the speed of sound or faster, they send out an ear-splitting shock wave, called sonic boom, that is capable of breaking window glass and cracking plaster walls. But no such effect has been observed from UFOs that fly silently even at speeds many times that of sound. After years of development at untold cost, the United States is now abandoning plans for a supersonic transport because of the sonic effect upon the environment, and it is leaving the global competition for marketing such planes to the joint British-French Concorde and the Russian TU-144. The technological achievement represented by UFOs in supersonic flight should certainly inspire awe and envy. It not only offers a means of avoiding sonic booms, but it implies a vast improvement in efficiency, since all the energy in sonic booms is a total waste. UFOs obviously suppress the formation of shock waves. Details are not available, but several points are clear. The presence of an approaching UFO must be "telegraphed" ahead to the gas molecules in the air. While yet some distance away, a small force must be exerted by the UFO to begin moving air molecules out of the way, becoming stronger as it comes nearer. After passage of the UFO, the air closes in behind. By such means, the UFO could slip through the atmosphere with little expenditure of energy, and no shock wave would be created on its leading edges. Apparently, the plasma on the surface of UFOs, or the radiant energy that stimulates it, is responsible. In 1968, Northrup Corporation was reportedly experimenting with electromagnetic fields to modify the air stream around supersonic aircraft to prevent shock waves.[15] Because the nose cone of an intercontinental ballistic missile generates a surrounding plasma upon reentering the atmosphere, the interaction between ICBMs and plasmas has been extensively researched, although the results are mostly classified. In a paper presented in 1968 to the Congressional Committee on Science and Astronautics, a scientist emphasized the extent of this literature. One reference alone abstracted over 800 publications on the subject.[16] He concluded that

> . . . there is a body of technology which I have studied and which leads me to believe that an entirely new approach to high speed air and space propulsion could be developed using the interactions between magnetic and electric fields with electrically conducting fluids adjacent to the vehicles to produce thrust or lift and reduce or eliminate such other hypersonic flight problems as drag, sonic boom, heating, etc.[17]

Wobble and Spin

As the entire vehicle or some major portion is sometimes observed to be spinning, several questions naturally arise. What is the purpose? Does the spinning have anything to do with the propulsion method? Do the rotating parts produce sound? Is the spinning limited to one or more specific types of vehicles? And so on. The only circumstance in which spinning has not been observed is when UFOs are resting on their landing gear. They sometimes start spinning as they lift off the grounds,[18] with a gradual increase in the rate of rotation.[19] No measure of the rate of spin is furnished in the data, but at least one witness indicated that it was rapid.[20] Objects were seen to be spinning while hovering,[21] during a car chase for 13 kilometers,[22] and in various speeds of descent toward the ground.[23] Most frequently it was reported that the entire object was spinning, and this was not limited to a particular type of craft, UFOs in the shapes of spheres, ovals, discs, and tops being included. Alternately, it was sometimes only a major component of the craft that was spinning, and this varied greatly in nature: an outer disc below a cabin,[24] a dome on top,[25] and the peripheral portion of a disc.[26] None of these instances can be correlated with a particular type of vehicle.

It is easy to imagine that rotation of the entire vehicle, or a major component, would be used to achieve stability in the air, that is, to maintain the axis of rotation in a constant direction due to the angular momentum. And this supposition is justified from the knowledge that disc-shaped aircraft are inherently unstable. In the early 1950s, millions of dollars were spent in developing a disc-shaped craft, the VZ-9V Avrocar, which was naively intended to be a real flying saucer. Designed to carry two men, it was 18 ft in diameter by 3.25 ft thick. Lift was obtained from a 5-ft-diameter turbomotor driven by three jet engines. It never got out of "ground effect" and it did "not in any instance have static aerodynamic stability."[27]

It is unthinkable that the passengers within a UFO would be subjected to the same rotation as the outer surface of the craft; hence, one must postulate a decoupling of the interior from the exterior portions. This is not to say that windows in the walls of a vehicle could not be party to the rotation. The pilot, in this situation, would have to stop the rotation in order to look out the window, as was implied in an incident in Wyoming. One night a rancher saw a shooting star come to a sudden stop in mid-air on his side of a mountain. It was rotating with a single window periodically facing toward him. Upon signaling the object with his headlamps, the rotation ceased with the window in his direction. After the resumption of spinning, the object maneuvered, then departed.[28] Not much clarity can be brought to this odd aspect of aerial behavior, but in summary, it can be said that UFOs sometimes spin at a moderate to rapid rate, either some prominent part or in toto. They have been seen to spin during all phases of flight but never while resting on the ground, a feature that is common to all types of UFOs. The rarity of these observations suggests that it is not a necessary adjunct to flight, but that it is used at the discretion of the pilot.

Evidences of Power

While the method of propulsion still remains a mystery, the literature conveys some impressions that are obviously related to it. Witnesses often experience a strong gust of air, either hot or cold, as the UFO sweeps past, descends, or takes off.[29] These gusts can be quite strong (at least one person was knocked off his feet).[30] Such currents would be expected from any large object moving swiftly through the air, but something else may be involved. The UFOs may exert a force directly on the air causing the reported gusts. Such a coupling is suggested by the behavior of vegetation under UFOs in flight—treetops that were spinning wildly,[31] violently moving plants,[32] and grass and plants that fluttered wildly.[33] Coconut palms were bent double under two UFOs that were taking off.[34] Loose materials are also effected: one UFO kicked up a small sand storm upon landing in a desert.[35] A low-flying UFO appeared to suck up snow as it passed overhead,[36] and snow swirled under another one.[37] The earth appeared to have been dug up at two landing sites,[38] while loose leaves were scattered from another.[39] Even waves of sea water peaked up toward a UFO hovering 15 meters above the surface.[40]

A car was pulled and rocked as a UFO hovering low above it left the scene.[41] While this motion could have been the result of a strong gust, none was mentioned in the report and some kind of direct, physical action on vehicles has been noted. A truck passed a government employee in Venezuela as a brilliant disc swooped close to its hood. The truck was lifted nearly 1 meter above the road and it was overturned in a sand bank.[42] Apparently the same experience befell a juvenile driver in Minnesota as he lost consciousness in the presence of a UFO. His truck was later discovered in a ditch facing the opposite direction.[43] Not only can a UFO apparently lift trucks off the road, it seems to impart a torque, or turning force to them, as confirmed by the spinning and swirling of other objects. The human body is not immune to this force, for a resident of Teheran testified that "I was standing with both hands on the bar of my balcony, looking with astonishment at this strange object, when I suddenly felt as though I were being drawn up toward the object by a magnet."[44] After being warned by a UFO pilot not to approach too closely, another witness inadvertently exposed his shoulder under the edge of a hovering craft. His arm was violently thrown up under the machine, then back down against his body. Although he could still move the arm after this accident, he had lost feeling in it.[45] A Frenchman remained outside the hazardous zone, although his horse did not. He was leading his mare with a bridle when a UFO took off from the side of the road and flew overhead. The mare rose about 3 meters into the air and the witness had to release the bridle. After falling back to the ground, the animal could not move for about 10 minutes.[46]

It is abundantly clear that a strange, hitherto unrecognized force prevails within a cylindrical zone having the same diameter as the UFO and extending from it to the ground. This force acts vertically upward upon various objects, imparting to them a rotation. As no stones or dry sticks seem to have been affected, the force apparently couples selectively to certain objects, presumably on the basis of their composition. Electrical conductivity is one feature common to the responsive items, namely, the human body, horse flesh, metals, and water. Snow and leaves would qualify if wet. If not wet, they would be blown around like desert sand. A direct coupling to the air would be possible through its content of water vapor and oxygen. Why the direction of this force should be upward is quite puzzling, since in more normal experience, jet exhausts batter downward. Yet, if the UFOs are defeating gravity by some means, it appears that they are sharing that achievement with objects in the region directly below them. These data should vastly encourage those theoreticians who see, in their equations, a statement of gravity damping by electromagnetic radiation.[47]

Still further evidence left on the ground by UFOs suggests exposure to intense heat in an unusual manner. The roots of grass were charred below a UFO hovering at low altitude, but the blades were not damaged. This odd effect was duplicated in an Air Force laboratory only by placing samples of living sod in a pan and heating from below to about 300°F. The principal investigator of this incident felt that the only way such an effect could be produced by a UFO from above was by induction heating from a "powerful, alternating magnetic field."[48] The merit of this concept will become clear presently. Heating is extremely common near UFOs. A deputy sheriff in Florida and a dozen other people felt their clothes burning them as one of six UFOs came close to a patrol car.[49] The clothes of a Belgian gardner were partially burned when he approached a landed UFO.[50] A heat wave filled a car in Louisiana, setting fire to, and completely destroying a 1956 Ford.[51] Trees were burned on two occasions.[52] A haystack was set ablaze by a passing UFO which also dessicated a small pond.[53] Evaporation of water was also noted on a rainy day when the trees, grass, and even ground were found to be completely dry where a recently departed UFO had hovered.[54] This preferential heating and evaporation of water is typical of microwaves, since water molecules absorb microwave energy very efficiently. As emission of microwaves from UFOs is encountered in several other contexts, it is hardly surprising here, and it almost certainly explains the charring of the grass roots without burning the blades. Many objects at landing sites were reportedly "calcined," that is, they had apparently been raised to high temperature with the resulting loss of volatile constituents. Examples include the ground itself,[55] insects,[56] a pole,[57] trees,[58] and matches.[59] As if this evidence were not enough, the record furnishes two instances in which UFOs taking off from bituminous highways set fire to the surface, which continued to burn for up to 15 minutes.[60] If the surface had been superficially heated to the kindling temperature, the volatile constituents would have been ignited but quickly consumed. Prolonged burning requires that the pavement, and probably the substratum, be heated in depth so that heat diffusing upward can maintain the temperature of the surface high enough to continue the supply of combustible gases. Such heating suggests bulk absorption of electromagnetic radiation of very high frequency.

One further detail of experience by witnesses seems to furnish helpful clues. A Libyan farmer saw an egg-shaped craft with a transparent upper half come to rest on a six-wheeled landing gear. Six men in yellowish coveralls could be seen on board. When the witness touched part of the craft, he suffered a strong electrical shock. One of the occupants motioned for him to stay away, and he watched for 20 minutes longer as they worked with instruments.[61] Similarly, a 13-year-old boy received a shock when he tried to touch an antenna on one of two small UFOs that he saw landing at Hamilton, Canada.[62] A prospector, also in Canada, watched a landed UFO for 30 minutes before seeing a door open. Upon approaching it he heard voices and tried to communicate, first in English then in several other languages. His rubber-coated glove was burned when he touched the craft.[63] Even though he later suffered burns when the UFO took off, there was no indication that the surface of the UFO was hot. The burning of his glove may have been some kind of electrical effect. The portions of the UFOs that were touched by the first two witnesses certainly carried electrical potentials relative to the ground. Some idea of the strength is afforded by the fact that neither of them was burned or killed. They would not have fared so well if the UFO had held a large, static charge at very high voltage, for its discharge to ground through the witnesses would have been grim. Also, the potentials could not have been very great or the electrified portions would have arched over to the portions in contact with the ground. At least modest voltages are implied, but it cannot be established whether they were static or alternating.

Microwave Propulsion

Within a variety of contexts in the preceding sections and chapters, the emanation of microwave energy from UFOs has been adduced. These references should be summarized here and examined together to improve the overall perspective of this point. Electromagnetic energy in the range of about 300 to 3,000 MHz, or higher, seemed to be responsible for:

a) stimulating colored halos around UFOs, largely from the noble gases in the atmosphere,

b) producing a dazzling, white plasma on the surface of UFOs, akin to ball lightning,

c) inducing chemical changes that were detected as odors,

d) turning off automobile headlights by increasing the resistance of their tungsten filaments,

e) stopping internal combustion engines by increasing resistance of the distributor points and suppressing the current in the primary windings,

f) precipitating wild gyrations of compasses and magnetic speedometers and rattling metallic road signs,

g) heating of automobile batteries through the direct absorption of energy in the acid,

h) interfering with radio (and television) reception and transmission by inducing extraneous voltages in the coil of the tuned circuit, or restricting the emission of electrons from tungsten cathodes,

i) disrupting transmission of electrical power by induced operation of isolation relays,

j) dessicating a small pond and drying of grass, bushes, and the ground by resonant absorption in water molecules,

k) charring or calcining grass roots, insects, and wooden objects at landing sites,

l) heating bituminous highways in depth and igniting the volatilized gases,

m) heating the human body internally,

n) causing people to feel electrical shocks, and

o) inducing temporary paralysis in the witnesses.

In addition, medical experiments have shown that, when pulsed at a low audio frequency this energy was capable of

p) stimulating the auditory nerve directly with the sensation of hearing a humming, or buzzing, sound.

While this evidence is so broad that the loss of a few points would hardly damage the argument, it is all circumstantial. Proof of the suspected radiation would be at hand only through direct, instrumental measurements by qualified personnel. But one despairs of the direct experimental approach in view of the difficulties in assembling the complex and expensive equipment, finding a UFO in the field, and staying in its vicinity long enough to make the measurements. Perhaps, the following episode can fill the present void.

A famous sighting in the fall of 1957 was made from an Air Force B-47 on a training mission over the Gulf of Mexico and the South-Central states. It came to the attention of the Condon Committee rather by accident and was investigated as Case No. 5. This UFO was seen by the pilot to be "as big as a barn" with a "steady, red glow" and it flew at speeds far greater than airplanes. It paced the aircraft through numerous changes of speed and seemed to jump instantly from one location to another. Visual sightings were coordinated with radar fixes from the air and the ground. The object emitted electromagnetic energy of about 2,800 MHz with "startling intensity." After the crew members had been interrogated upon completion of the flight, the "security lid" came down on the incident and no records could be found, not even in Project Blue Book.[64]

More successful research was reported by an enterprising private investigator to the 136th Meeting of the American Association for the Advancement of Science at Boston in December 1969. As the entire episode is very intricate, only highlights of special importance are reviewed here. The aircraft, equipped for electronic countermeasures missions, was returning from a flight over the Gulf of Mexico when it first encountered the UFO near Meridian, Mississippi. The UFO played tag with the aircraft at various speeds greater than 500 mph and literally flew circles around it. The contact lasted for 1.5 hours as the plane flew across Mississippi, Louisiana, northern Texas, and making a large loop near Ft. Worth before turning northward into Oklahoma. Upon losing contact near Oklahoma City, the B-47 proceeded to its home field, Forbes AFB in northeastern Kansas. The B-47 was released from its assigned mission to chase the UFO, and the FAA cleared other jet traffic from the area. Observation of the UFO was confirmed through at least five independent physical channels, namely, visually from the cockpit, navigation radar on board, two airborne electronic countermeasure receivers, and military ground control radar. Electronic equipment on the aircraft of primary interest here was monitor no. 2, operated by an Air Force officer named McClure. It consisted of an ALA-6DF passive receiver with back-to-back antennas in a housing on the belly of the plane having spin rates of 150 to 300 rpm in scanning the azimuth. Incoming signals were displayed on an APR-9 radar receiver and fed into an ALA-5 pulse analyzer. An official report by the Wing Intelligence Officer at Forbes AFB in reference to the UFO said:

> . . . intercepted at approximately Meridian, Mississippi, a signal with the following characteristics; frequency 2995 MC to 3000 MC; pulse width of 2.0 microseconds; pulse repetition frequency of 600 cps; sweep rate of 4 rpm; vertical polarity . . . Signal moved rapidly up the DF scope indicating a rapidly moving signal source; i.e., an airborne source. . . .

These signal characteristics were confirmed on monitor no. 1, but nothing was detected on monitor no. 3 which was scanning lower frequency ranges.[65]

This UFO was, in fact, pouring forth large amounts of electromagnetic radiation in a very narrow range of the microwave region, and it was pulsed at a low audio rate!

McClure recalled that the signal characteristics bore a strong similarity to ground-based sets such as the CPS-6B that were widely used at that time. But it is untenable to assert that somebody installed a large search radar in a barn-sized machine and flew circles around a B-47. Nor was the UFO merely utilizing its own radar to keep an eye on the airplane. It was previously shown that radiant energy produced colored halos and plasmas around UFOs which changed in accordance with their accelerations, that is, the application of power. Hence, the conclusion from this B-47 incident is inescapable. The flood of microwave energy from the UFO was an essential, integral part of a propulsion system that is common to all UFOs. This system by some unknown means is capable of diminishing or nullifying gravitational and inertial forces; it also furnishes the requisite thrust for acceleration, and moves air out of the flight path to minimize drag and, above sonic velocities, to eliminate shock waves.

It would be helpful if the total amount of energy radiated by this UFO could be estimated, but unfortunately no quantitative data on this point is included in the report. Suitable information, however, can be gleaned from a few other reports. Two peasant farmers in Brazil, upon hearing a strange hum, saw two aluminum discs about 10 ft in diameter that were hovering close to the ground at a distance of 200 meters.[66] If the humming sound were induced within their heads by pulses of microwave energy, as suggested by the word ''strange,'' then the irradiation to which they were exposed must have been as high as the threshold for that effect, known to be 0.333 milliwatts per square centimeter.[67] Since the UFOs were hovering instead of resting on the ground, their power systems must have been in operation. In the absence of better information, energy emission from them is assumed to have been equal in all directions. The report contains no indication that a concentrated beam was directed toward the witnesses. Finally, the degradation of intensity over the distance of 200 meters from the UFOs to the witnesses can be closely approximated by the inverse square law. All the necessary factors are present, or assumed, to calculate the total energy emanating from the UFOs that passes through an imaginary sphere of 200-m radius. The resulting value is 1.6 megawatts. To put this amount into some perspective, the maximum energy that may be broadcast by a local radio station is limited by the Federal Communications Commission to 0.5 megawatt. Put another way, diesel locomotives up to 2,000 hp are most popular for express freight service in North America. The electrical power equivalent of this rating is about 1.5 megawatts. Thus the two UFOs in a state of hovering were generating and emitting several times the amount of energy that is broadcast by the most powerful radio stations, or an amount comparable to the power of a diesel locomotive. Of course this estimate pertains only to the minimum value, and it would not be valid at all if the humming sound were detected by normal hearing. At least it illustrates a point of view that, upon broad application to many sightings, should yield fairly reliable results.

Limits of Theory

Previous discussions have shown that the propulsion system in UFOs relies upon unknown mechanisms to reduce their effective mass with a twofold advantage, furnishing lift through nullifying gravity and achieving enormous accelerations with only moderate forces. While this performance is compatible with well-established theory, it is greatly in advance of current technology. It does not appear to be so far distant that a well-organized and adequately funded research program would not make it available to humanity. Even though daily experience impresses everyone with the persistence and strength of gravity, it is actually extremely weak in comparison to the other fields in nature. Overcoming it should not be too troublesome if one could only discover how. As electromagnetic fields have an energy density, they are influenced by gravity, but the effect is very small. Otherwise, electrical and magnetic fields interpenetrate gravitational fields without the slightest influence one way or the other. A major theoretical difficulty is encountered in the observation that UFOs are defeating gravity by an electromagnetic field. Neither in the laboratory nor in nature has any such gross interaction ever been observed. It has long been suspected in theoretical circles, however, that all natural fields are related and that they interact in some way. This relationship is part of a problem known as unified field theory in which some impressive advances have been made but completely satisfying solutions are still wanting. Very advanced mathematical concepts have been used to describe a gravitational field from which electromagnetic fields can be derived, although the latter do not appear explicitly in the original form. Unfortunately, the trail of elucidating the performance of UFOs ends here. Their behavior, however, represents some new empirical data that, upon examination from a theoretical perspective, may produce the mutual benefits of improving the theory and understanding UFOs.[68]

But the facts must be recorded
—they may be only interesting
bits of folklore—or they may in-
volve the future of civilization.
                    — Jacques Vallee

CHAPTER 8

PILOTS AND PASSENGERS

The observation of strange, human-like creatures in and about UFOs is an integral part of the entire phenomenon and this aspect can hardly be ignored simply because it is a disquieting notion. Indeed, "it may yet be discovered that humanoid cases are the key to the whole problem."[1] While observations of the humanoids are traceable well back into history, it was not until the modern era of UFOs, beginning about 1947, that people began to write extensively about their encounters. Many of them told about observing the humanoids at close range, communicating with them, establishing a personal rapport, and consorting with them for extended periods. Messages of peace from the "space brothers" and warnings about atomic bombs were typically reported. Except for limited cults that developed around the authors, this literature was generally shrugged off as completely unbelievable. It will not be neglected here.

Intense prejudice against UFO reports has prevailed for over twenty years with a vicious intensity against those involving the so-called "little green men" and the "contactee" cases. Under a threat of ridicule, such experiences were usually discussed only among families and friends. Whenever reported to the authorities, they received little serious attention. Most such reports were dismissed outright on the grounds that the witnesses must have been mistaken, lying, or unbalanced. Officers responsible for investigating UFO reports at each Air Force base would be reluctant to forward such silliness through channels, and those reports reaching Project Blue Book faired poorly. Some were simply discarded while others were merely tallied without investigation in categories such as "psychological."[2] "Good UFO reports continued to come in at the rate of about ten per month, but they weren't verified or investigated. Most of them were being discarded."[3] Regrettably, a considerable amount of valuable information has been lost.

It is not intended in this chapter to debate the existence of UFO creatures. The author takes this question as settled, either permanently or tentatively. In either event, this mental attitude permits an unbiased examination of the available data; the value of the inquiry can be measured by the sense that it makes of an initially baffling subject. The data bank consists of 891 cases of landings and near-landings during the twentieth century; thirty-two cases prior to 1900 are omitted because they contain many sightings of a mysterious airship in the United States that are atypical of UFOs. Inclusion of these few reports, however, would not materially alter the following results.[4]

As found in other aspects of the UFO problem, accounts of the occupants are extremely variable. They are seldom quantitative, and almost never complete. A rational analysis of such fragmentary and unscientific data is itself a challenge. But regarding the size of the occupants, perusal of the reports clearly shows at least two distinct groups; one is diminutive while the other is apparently of normal height. Descriptive words that do not carry any connotation of size, such as "figure" and "being," must simply be ignored. Qualitative terms can be sorted and tallied; that is, average height is denoted by "man," "normal," and "human," whereas decisive shortness is denoted by "little man," "child-size," and "dwarf." As the two groups are distinguished by different facial details, some cases can be assigned to the appropriate category whenever the creatures are described but their height is not mentioned. The remaining reports are either entirely silent regarding the height of the creatures or contain estimated heights, that is, some quantitative data. Should a rough statistical analysis of these data confirm the presence of two distinct size categories as previously inferred, one is justified in combining the tallies from the quantitative and qualitative cases.

The following diagram shows the frequency of estimated heights, in intervals of tenths of meters, for the 81 cases containing quantitative data. It also compares the estimates with the range of heights that is considered by anthropologists to be normal for human populations. A preponderance of small creatures below the lower limit for normal humans is obvious. Some estimates are scattered within the normal range. Still a few others indicate very tall giants. As the full-range distribution of heights gives no hint that the extremes are the rarely occurring instances within a single population, it appears that three distinct populations are represented, that is, diminutive, normal, and giant.

Diminutives

A population of small creatures is indicated in the diagram by the roughly bell-shaped envelope of the vertical bars. Sixty-one of the 81 cases containing quantitative data indicate dwarves. In addition, 58 other cases refer to dwarves in qualitative terms. Thus, 119 cases involve dwarves. But the total number of dwarves is much greater than 119 because they were commonly observed in pairs and sometimes in groups of 5 to 10. The most frequently occurring estimate of height was 1.0 meter, having been used 16 times in the 81 reports. Almost all the small group were estimated to be between 0.7 and 1.3 meters tall, well below the lower limit of normalcy for humans. Dispersion of the data can arise from inaccuracy of the witness in estimating heights or from an actual variation in the heights of the little creatures. If all the small creatures were exactly 1 meter tall, could witnesses be as far off in their estimates as, say, 0.5 or 1.5 meters? It seems

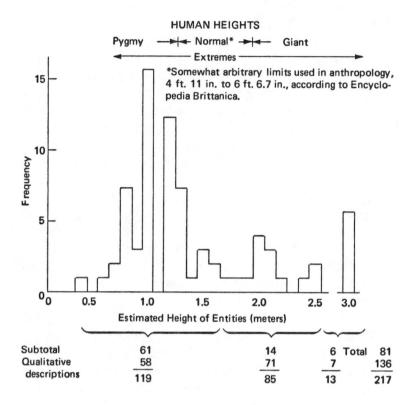

HUMAN HEIGHTS

Pygmy ——▶|◀— Normal* —▶|◀— Giant

◀———————— Extremes ————————▶

*Somewhat arbitrary limits used in anthropology, 4 ft. 11 in. to 6 ft. 6.7 in., according to Encyclopedia Brittanica.

Frequency

Estimated Height of Entities (meters)

Subtotal	61	14	6 Total	81
Qualitative descriptions	58	71	7	136
	119	85	13	217

very unlikely. A significant factor in the dispersion should therefore be attributed to variation in the heights of individuals in the group. An isolated estimate of 0.33 meters may be spurious. Assuming that it is, the weighted average for the diminutive group up to 1.5 meters is 1.05 meteres (3ft 5in) or, say, 3 feet, which confirms a recent estimate.[5] As a point of reference, it is noted that the standard height of doorknobs is 3.0 feet.

A predominance of estimates of about 80 centimeters is especially interesting. Six of these sightings were reported from the vicinity of Arequipa in southern Peru and the vicinity of Rio de Janeiro, Brazil, all in the month of September 1965.[6] At Puno,

Peru, near Lake Titacaca, seven of these very small people were seen together, and at Pichaca, six. Other reports for this size group originated from England in June of the previous years,[7] and from Reunion Island in the Indian Ocean three years later.[8] The smallest individuals, estimated to be 0.33 meters on one occasion and 0.50 meter on another, are indeed very tiny—only 13 to 20 inches! But such heights are not altogether unreasonable. The human malady known as ateliotic or infantile dwarfism, produces very small individuals. In this type of dwarfism, the skeleton tends to remain in the infantile state with the resulting body proportions being nearly normal. The most famous ateliotic dwarf was certainly Charles Sherwood Stratton, billed as General Tom Thumb by the circus magnate, P. T. Barnum. When 18 years old, standing 2ft 9in tall, recently made his U.S. debut in grow throughout his life, reaching 40 inches at the time of his death at age 51. Jozef "Count" Boruwlaski was only 25 inches tall at the age of 15. He reached his maximum growth of 39 inches at the age of 30 and lived for 97 years. The shortest adult male on record, however, was Calvin Phillips, who two years before his death at age 21 was 26.5 inches tall. A Dutch female was even smaller; Pauline Masters was only 23.2 inches tall when she died at age 19.[9] The smallest man alive today is believed to be the Hungarian circus performer, Mihaly Mezaros, who at 34 years old standing 2ft 9in tall, recently made his U.S. debute in Madison Square Garden.[10] These tiny humans are, of course, very rare individuals and not indicative of a small species. However, many races of diminutive people are known.

The more common achondroplastic dwarfism displaying characteristic features known as the "bulldog syndrome," is seen in all human races and in many animal species. Notable features are a disproportionately large head and short face with bulbous forehead, broad nose, and bulging eyes. Shortened bones of the forearm and lower leg are also typical. African pygmies sometimes have these characteristics, the smallest race being the North Twides of the Ituri forest, their mean heights being 1.44 m for the men and 1.37 m for the women.[11] A similar sexual dimorphism in the small UFO creatures is suggested by the double-peaked histogram, with males being slightly over 1 meter and females slightly under.

Certain environmental factors favor the evolutionary reduction in sizes of all animal species. Among these are the combined effects of overcrowding, limited area of habitation, and inadequate nutrition. In areas of high temperature and high humidity, small size is an advantage because the body can maintain its thermal equilibrium more easily. The evaporative cooling by skin moisture is restricted by high humidity, and a small body has a larger ratio of surface area to volume. The agility of small bodies is also an advantage in areas where dense vegetation impedes movement. Of the numerous dwarf species, a few examples will suffice: an extinct dwarf mammoth of Santa Rosa Island, California, a dwarf deer of Japan, a dwarf chimpanzee of the Belgian Congo, and the Negrito Onge pygmies of Little Andaman Island in the Indian Ocean.[12]

It is most instructive to build a composite concept of the bodily features for this group from the 23 cases in which some description was offered. Although the available detail is distressingly limited, several features were repeatedly mentioned. Abnormally large heads were described as "big," "double-sized," "oversized," "huge," and "large." Similarly, the eyes were observed to be "bulging," "huge," and "prominent." Other comments give an impression of a generally human appearance, very thin limbs, barely noticeable mouth and nose, but large, pointed ears. Several colors of skin were mentioned, but "green" only once. From other sources it seems that the skin is wrinkled, the lips are very thin, the forehead protrudes, and long arms carry normal hands with long fingernails.[13] A few comments by the witnesses are simply incomprehensible—"short tail," "short wings," and "one eye."

The appearance of this group may be summarized as thin, human-like creatures approximately 1.0 meter tall, with abnormally large, bald heads and large, round, bulging eyes that are set wide apart. A protruding forehead with wrinkled skin adds to

118

their ugliness. On a short face, only nostrils are evident instead of a fully developed nose. The mouth is but a horizontal slit. Ears are large and pointed. Arms and fingernails are long.

Certain aspects of this description strongly suggest that the race of little people on UFOs are pygmies displaying many of the typical characteristics of achondroplastic dwarfism. By frequent use of the word "dwarf," the witnesses have apparently been trying to convey more than just the idea of their size. They actually mean "dwarf." It is further implied that the little people did not have an independent lineage but that their environmental conditions caused them to evolve into a dwarf race from larger ancestors. Their appearance, therefore, may be a significant clue to environmental conditions in their homeland and their place in the scheme of evolution.

Normals

In addition to the population of small beings associated with UFOs, a distinctly different group can be identified. They seem to be quite human and display none of the characteristic features of the dwarves. These beings were reported in 85 instances out of the total of 217; again, their actual number is greater than 85 as they were sometimes seen in pairs and small groups. In most of the reports, witnesses were not explicit in referring to their stature; the previous diagram shows that their heights were estimated only 14 times. Estimated values cover the normal range for humans and extend beyond, both shorter and taller.

A few estimates of about 1.5 meters are troublesome as they may pertain to either the dwarves or the larger beings, and the available data in these cases do not always permit a clear distinction. The distribution of sizes among both groups may also overlap at about 1.5 meters, so that some of these estimates are for the largest dwarves whereas others are for the smallest "normals." A sharp cutoff between the heights of the two groups cannot be established.

Very tall individuals were also reported with estimated heights up to 2.5 meters, about 8 feet. While certainly abnormal for humans, such height is not unheard of. At the age of 22 years, Robert Pershing Wadlow of Alton, Illinois, was 8 ft 11.1 in. tall. Seven other males over 8 ft tall are also on record. These individuals suffered from an overactive pituitary gland. A non-pathological example, however, is Angus MacAskill. He lived in the Outer Hebrides, Scotland, from 1825 to 1863 and grew to 7-ft 9-in.[14] Average-size people are much impressed by very tall people and tend to overestimate their height. Circus giants are sometimes billed as being considerably taller than their actual height, which they are under contract not to reveal. Thus the extreme heights of this group may be somewhat exaggerated.

Not much detail is available concerning the appearance of this group. It may be that they are so completely human that nothing unusual about them attracted attention. The witness simply identified them as "normal" or "human," sometimes indicating their approximate size as "short," "medium," or "very tall." One witness might mention the hair color while another comments only about a peculiarity of the eyes. The scarcity of detail may also be attributed to a propensity of this group to wear headgear that would obscure facial details. In 18 cases witnesses reported "helmets" or the equivalent with more graphic language describing a globular shape such as "diving suit with helmet" and "fishbowl." Despite the meager data, a composite image of the group can be evoked.

Predominantly reported skin colors, arranged by shade, are: "very white," "white," "fair," "tanned," "light brown," and "brown." With the aid of a further observation that one chap seemed to be "European," the imagination is not unduly strained to suppose that the group is a white race displaying various degrees of suntan. Two odd and conflicting observations occurred. One witness reporting "reddish-orange" skin also commented upon a "strange light" seen through an open door on the UFO. And then one saw "greenish" skin on an individual who was dressed in a green uniform. Perhaps the extraneous tinges were picked up from the surroundings, as a human face takes on a purple hue when illuminated by mercury-arc lamps.

Relatively frequent mention was made of the hair, regarding both the color and styling. Most common descriptions are "long" and "blond." One witness kindly put these notions together with "fair" hair "to the shoulders." In addition, isolated reports included two men with "short white" hair and two women with "very long black" hair. Incidently, the presence of women was specifically noted on five occasions.

Three witnesses said that the eyes were "slanted," whereas numerous other comments were supplied, such as "dark," "large," "deep-set," "staring," "round" and "wide apart." In none of these instances were the witnesses confused regarding the number of eyes, namely, two; but "one eye" and "three eyes" were also reported. While these latter reports may be accurate, it seems more likely that the witnesses were misled by some kind of headgear.

Some impressions of the general appearance were "oversized head," "high forehead," and "handsome," "long face" and "youthful." Regarding noses and ears there is absolutely no information. Except, perhaps, for a creature of 1.5 meters who reportedly had no nose. As that feature is common among the dwarves and the height is in the zone of overlap, that report probably does not pertain to the present group. It may be assumed that noses and ears have no unusual features, because they elicited no comments.

While this group may be much more heterogeneous than is currently suspected, a possibly oversimplified prototype comes into focus. The group seems to be a white, Caucasian race of variable skin tone, perhaps depending upon the extent of suntan. Their heights are comparable to ordinary humans, but the range is somewhat broader, inclining to very tall individuals. Their hair is predominantly blonde and usually worn at shoulder length. Eyes have a slight oriental appearance, whereas nothing unusual is to be noted about the noses and ears.

With the exception of a single instance,[15] occurring in Denmark in 1951, all encounters with the large humanoids in the data bank were preceded by an incident on a California desert. On November 20, 1952, a witness met a strange man face-to-face in broad daylight who was described as "completely human," "5 feet 6 inches" tall, and weighing about "135 pounds." He had a "medium-colored suntan," "extremely high forehead," and his "sandy" hair fell "to his shoulders" blowing in the wind. His eyes were "large grey-green, slightly aslant at the outer corners," nose "finely chiseled," and mouth "normal." After some friendly gesturing, drawing of diagrams in the sand, and telepathic communication, the two men walked over to a UFO hovering nearby. The stranger climbed aboard and flew away.[16] In other words, the composite picture of normal-size, UFO pilots seen on at least 83 occasions between 1952 and 1968 confirms the image of this class of being's as described by the witness, George Adamski.

Giants

The previous histogram indicated that on six separate occasions the UFO creatures were estimated to be 3.0 meters tall, or about 10 feet. Even allowing for some exaggeration by the witnesses, they were truly gigantic! But bear in mind that they are not a great deal taller than others who, up to 8 feet tall, seemed in every respect to be members of the "normal" population. Do these very tall people represent another race, or are they merely extreme examples of the same group?

These reports clearly belong to the UFO phenomenon, for one of the giants was seen inspecting his craft. Three others climbed out of a large UFO that blocked the highway directly in front of the witnesses' truck. A few observations concerning clothing, helmets, and boots seem to parallel the other cases. Rare comments such as "ugly," "no nose or mouth," and "one eye" are perplexing and suggest a distinctly non-human appearance. However, the data for these cases is too sketchy to conclude that the "giants" are a separate race. They must be considered as very large individuals of the so-called normal group. If this classification is correct, the concept of "normal" must certainly be broadened to encompass the full range of heights from about 5 feet to nearly 10 feet.

The possibility of a racial distinction within this group intrudes here but it should be considered as improbable. The vast majority have been described as completely human whereas the occasional references to grotesque features seems to apply to all sizes. Thus two races may be represented within this range of heights that are distinguishable by their appearance, that is, normal versus beings with bizarre facial features.

Relationships

As a minimum, the evidence clearly indicates two distinct races inhabiting UFOs, namely, the dwarves and normal humans that are sometimes very tall. One wonders whether these two races are traveling independently about the earth, whether they are aware of each other, and if so, whether their relationship is friendly, indifferent, or hostile. A shopkeeper in Argentina, who was prone to unusual experiences, reported that he had entered a UFO in which he saw four crew members "less than one meter in height"; a "fifth member was a blond man almost two meters in height." Some college students in Mexico City claimed that a tall man with "fair hair and blue eyes" invited them aboard a UFO. After a three-hour flight they reached a space station that was occupied by many "beings who differed greatly among themselves as to size and appearance." The beings were allegedly from various planets. Another UFO occupant over 6 ft tall reportedly told a Brazilian author that "there were not only tall races" in his homeland "but also races of medium-size like earth people, and small races, but also races with white, red, and black pigmentation . . ."[17]

The races certainly seem to be on speaking terms. Despite the conflict concerning origins in the above reports, the most natural supposition is that they come from the same place and are cooperating in their ventures.

Languages

With so many people encountering the UFO races at close range, it would be surprising if someone had not overheard them conversing amongst themselves, or even addressing the witness. Such is indeed the case. The record indicates at least 26 occasions when the speech of the dwarves was heard. Usually the witness could not understand their language.

Developing some further insight into this situation presents some difficulty, for 16 instances involving unintelligible language occurred in several countries, namely, United States (2), France (7), Brazil (1), Great Britian (1), Canada (1), and Italy (4). In any of these instances, the dwarf speaking a language other than that native in the country would not normally be understood. Hence these data do not require that the dwarves have their own separate languages, as they might well be speaking French in Brazil or Chinese in West Virginia. A race like the dwarves, however, presumably isolated from the main stream of humanity for some time, would be expected to develop and use a unique language. Some hint of this circumstance is provided by the following descriptions of the language used by the dwarves, even though not understood by the witnesses.

Description	Case	Country
pointed, childlike voices	46	Canada
grunting like pigs	137	France
inhuman	147	France
gutteral sounds	331	Italy
chattering	434	United States
strange tones as if it came from a pipe	617	United States
shrill sounds similar to a gargle	650	France
strange, musical dialect	855	France

These descriptions do not suggest that the dwarves were merely speaking an ordinary language that was unfamiliar to the witnesses, as attested by "strange" and "inhuman." "Childlike" and "shrill" denote a high-pitched voice befitting small beings, while "like pigs," "guttural," and "gargle" denote a harsh quality of sounds produced in the throat. The language of the dwarves is probably unique and unintelligible in any country.

In any event, at least one word used by the dwarves can be identified and defined. One dwarf communicated, presumably by gesture, that his craft was called a "sil."[18] Another one could not get through to an Italian with something like "Dbano da skigyay o dbano," but he may have been merely asking directions to the nearest bathroom.[19]

The dwarves are unimpressive as linguists, but a few have spoken to the witnesses in their native tongues, using: Spanish in Argentina, Venezuela, and Mexico; English in Nebraska, New York, South Carolina, New Jersey, and California; and Italian, naturally in Italy. As might be expected, the language skills varied considerably among the individual dwarves. Their English was variously described as "broken," "very smooth," and "perfect." Similarly, Spanish on one occasion was spoken "slowly and with difficulty," whereas a more fluent colleague was rated "perfect." A dwarf speaking Spanish in Mexico strung "the words together in a strange accent." It seems fairly clear that English and Spanish are secondary languages of the dwarves, which they have learned and are in the process of improving.

If any intelligible messages came through to a witness in his own language he should be eager to tell what the dwarf had said. After such an unusual tete-a-tete, most of them are. Statements attributed to the dwarves are that they are "from space," they would "meet again" with the witness, they are "peaceful people," and have "philanthropic and scientific purposes." These messages, taken together, seem to be quite reasonable.

The dwarves seem to carry on normal conversations among themselves and sometimes talk to the witnesses in an incomprehensible language. This language seems unique to the dwarves and consists of guttural sounds of high pitch. Some of them apparently have mastered to various degrees the more common languages, such as, English, Spanish, and Italian. Perhaps they are also learning French, Russian, and the Oriental languages but the evidence is not available.

The normal, human types aboard UFOs display somewhat greater linguistic ability than the dwarves, as indicated in 30 instances involving languages and other communication. They were incomprehensible to witnesses in only 12 cases—an impressive performance, indeed, considering the range of countries in which they landed and spoke. Cases occurred in Italy, United States, Wales, New Zealand, Peru, Great Britian, Japan, Brazil, Portugal, Argentina, and Azores. When witnesses did not recognize the language used by the visitors, they very commonly attempted to describe it. A 12-year-old boy in Tennessee thought it sounded "like German," although it is not reported how familiar he was with that language. Also, one should bear in mind that it might have been German or nearly anything other than English. Two independent descriptions of the language of this group, "shrill" and "metallic," are reminiscent of the sound of the language used by the dwarves. Perhaps they are one and the same. This supposition is nurtured by the apparent cooperation of the two races.

A foreign-looking woman appeared at the door of a sanatorium in Brazil holding "a mug and a glass bottle covered with beautiful engravings." She uttered something like "Rempaua." The containers were filled with water and returned to her. With apparent satisfaction, the strange woman departed and boarded a UFO that took off.[20] If the word spoken by the woman cannot be identified in earthly language, it might belong to her native tongue. In another Brazilian incident, a survey worker and his associates saw a great disc landing. After his friends had fled, the witness encountered three strange-looking and oddly dressed creatures that were 7 ft tall. With a stick, one of them made seven holes in the ground surrounding a larger hole. The center hole was called "Alamo" and the most distant hole, "Orque." The Sun and Uranus, respectively, have been proposed as the meanings of these words.[21] While the opportunities to make such inferences are extremely rare, considerable progress has been made in compiling a lexicon of the language used by the UFO people.[22]

The larger races appear to be more successful in communicating in the languages of the witnesses. Individuals of this group have used the following languages in appropriate countries: Italian, English, Portugese, French, and Spanish. Their messages in the composite seem similar to those reported for the dwarves. Familiar expressions included "peaceful purposes," "we will return," "from space," and "carrying out a mission on earth." Witnesses were sometimes invited aboard the UFO, or warned not to touch it. One invitation was accompanied by a threat.[23] Less sinister discussions involved general questions about the witness and inquiries concerning directions and location. While allegedly on board a giant UFO, a Mexican student was told in Spanish that the UFO races knew 700 earth languages.[24] Notwithstanding this boast, two of the visitors seemed ill-prepared to land their vehicle on the southern coast of Brazil. Sitting nearby was a lawyer, who was also a Professor of Law and obviously an accomplished linguist. He asked the two strangers where they came from "in Portugese, Italian, Spanish, French, and English," but elicited no verbal response.[25]

This same professor, however, perceived a telepathic invitation to board the craft and he did. After a pleasant flight lasting 30 to 40 minutes, he was returned to the place where he had been picked up. Such telepathy—the reception of a message in the brain without benefit of a spoken language—is rather commonly reported. An extended, two-way communication by this method was reported in 1952.[26] Sometimes an unintelligible language is involved but the message still comes through. In Brazil in 1954, for example, a witness saw "two men of slim build, normal height, their faces brownish, wearing no helmets." One was collecting samples of grass and the other was inside a machine shaped like a football about the size of a Volkswagen. He could not understand what they said, but he knew that they wanted some ammonia.[27] One of four teachers in a car-stopping incident in France perceived the word "Zemu" repeated twice.[28] In one spooky case, an apparition in a woman's house moved his lips, but nothing was heard. The woman, however, understood that the visitor was from space and was searching for titanium under the oceans.[29]

While information concerning the languages and communication of the normal-looking UFO people is quite sketchy, a few points seem to be reasonably clear. They seem to have a unique, unearthly language that is used mostly in talking to one another. This language is probably the same as that used by their smaller friends. Both groups sometimes converse with witnesses in several of the familiar earth languages. They usually say that they mean no harm, are from space, and are conducting investigations on earth. Frequent invitations to board their craft are issued, but they are sometimes accompanied by a sinister implication or an actual threat. A message is occasionally conveyed, even though the language is not understood by the witness, or even if no language is used at all.

Clothing

Some information about the clothing of the UFO people is usually reported. The amount of detail may vary greatly among the reports, depending upon the distance from the beings, the duration of the sightings, and lighting conditions, and the extent to which the attention of the witness may have been drawn to other aspects of a spectacular event. The individual's power of observation and level of interest in clothing certainly influenced the content of his report. At any rate, enough observations have been recorded to develop a composite and fairly clear concept of the clothing of the UFO people, including some interesting details about accessories such as belts, headgear, boots, and gloves.

Among the 447 close encounters during the decade from November 1958 to November 1968, 123 instances involved sightings of human-like creatures.[30] When the distance was too great or the light too dim, the witnesses could only indefinitely describe "man," "figures," or "little boys." Such sightings without detail occurred about 50% of the time. It is in the remaining 50%, comprising 63 instances, that some specific data is to be found.

Body Covering

Witnesses almost always refer to the clothing of the UFO people as "coveralls," that is, a one-piece garment with long sleeves and pant legs. Other terms such as "diver's suit" and "like a pilot" help to clarify the idea. The fit seems to vary from skin-tight to comfortably loose. A wide range of observed colors includes gray, white, black, gold, blue, silver, red and "luminous." On several occasions the surface texture was seen to be "shiny." A suit appeared to be transparent to one witness, but he supplied no further details. These garments were obviously uniforms, as the UFO people, when seen in groups, nearly always dressed alike. No distinction can be discerned in the reports between the clothing of the dwarves and the larger people.

On rare occasions, more casual attire was noted. In the presence of a companion in the common coverall *one dwarf wore a "gray shirt and brown trousers."* [31] Three dwarves were all seen wearing "purple jerseys and white shirts." [32] A salesman in West Virginia stopped his car close to a large UFO hovering above the roadway directly ahead. A man of dark complexion came out wearing "a shirt and ordinary trousers, both a shiny blue color . . ." [33] A rather small man looked positively natty when he climbed out of his craft in Wisconsin wearing "a black, turtle-neck pullover with a white band at the belt, and black trousers with a vertical white band along the side." [34]

Not once were any pockets, seams, buttons, or zippers mentioned. On the contrary, when a witness had an opportunity to see such details, he sometimes pointedly reported their absence. A witness in South Africa, who peered at the pilot of a landed UFO through a port hole, said that "he wore a sky-blue, one-piece coverall with no visible buttons or fasteners." [35] Similarly, no seams could be detected by a farmer in New York while talking to two dwarves at a distance of only 5 feet, and he mentioned it.[36] It seems clear that the "coveralls" do not have pockets, seams, buttons, or the like.

Belts

Wide belts are a popular accessory to the standard, one-piece uniform, but certain strange features suggest purposes other than securing the trousers, a function that would be superfluous for a one-piece garment. An Italian observer met two men near a dazzling UFO, with belts emitting intermittent yellow-green-blue light.[37] Four months later, the same man again saw two more figures with luminous belts, but the light was so bright he could not make out any other detail.[38] A utilitarian aspect of the belts was demonstrated in Venezuela by two beings about 2 meters tall. Their belts emitted light rays and they refrained from touching anything without first illuminating it with these beams.[39] It is possible that they were merely using the beams as a flashlight; however, the following episode from Mexico indicates something entirely different.

A taxicab broke down on a main highway one rainy evening in 1953 and the driver could not repair it. He sat in the vehicle all night talking with two strangers who were wearing wide, shiny, perforated belts. At first, the driver thought that the strangers were pilots from some other Latin American country, but one of them told him in Spanish that they came from a far distant planet. At dawn, all three walked to a craft about one-half kilometer across swampy terrain. The witness sank deep into mud but the legs and feet of the strangers remained clean. He explained that "When their feet touched the muddy pools *their belts glowed and the mud sprang away as if repelled by some invisible force.*"[40] The strangers were also wearing metal collars around their necks and small, black, shiny boxes on their backs. As these latter two items are very rarely reported, they are probably associated with the belts and with this unusual incident. Had the invisible force been applied with more intensity, the strangers undoubtedly would have risen completely off the ground. In other words, the belts are probably part of a system that acted against gravity to keep their wearers from sinking and that simultaneously scattered the mud. One suspects, however, that the primary purpose of the system is to furnish propulsion for flying in a way comparable to a rocket system that American soldiers wear on their backs. While flying is not the most popular method used by the UFO people in getting around, they have been observed on many occasions to hover, or to zoom through the air in a most perplexing way. Specific examples are cited in the section on Personal Locomotion.

It may be worthwile at this juncture to compare the composite view of clothing developed above with that attributed to a UFO pilot some years previously.

His clothing was a one-piece garment which I had a feeling was a uniform worn by space men as they travel, liek Earth men in various types of work-wear uniforms to indicate their occupations.

Its colour was chocolate brown and it was made with a rather full blouse, close-fitting high collar much like a turtle neck, only it did not turn down. The sleeves were long, slightly full and similar to a Raglan sleeve, with closefitting bands around the wrists.

A band about eight inches in width circled his waist. And the only break in colouring of the entire garment was a strip about an inch and a half in width at the top and bottom of this waistband. This was brighter and more of a golden brown.

"The trousers were rather full and held in at the ankles with bands like those on the sleeves at the wrists, in style much like a ski pant.

Actually it is very difficult to describe this garment in colouring for I know of no descriptive word in our language that would suit it perfectly.

It was definitely a woven material, very fine, and the weave was different from any of our materials. There was a sheen about the whole garment, but I could not tell whether or not this was due to a finishing process or whether it might be the kind of substance of which its thread was made. It was not like our satin, silk, or rayon, for it had more of a radiance than a sheen.

I saw no zippers, buttons, buckles, fasteners or pockets of any kind, nor did I notice seams as our garments show. It is still a mystery to me how his garment was made.[41]

As the witness, George Adamski, thoroughly anticipated numerous, unrelated events around the world for two decades, he was either accurately describing a personal observation, or he was one of the best prophets of modern times. Other portions of his writings certainly deserve to be scrutinized for information about UFOs.

Helmets

It is rather common for the UFO people to be seen wearing helmets. In Wisconsin, a man stepped out of an elevator suspended beneath a UFO "with something like a glass fishbowl on his head."[42] Other observations confirm the general features of this accessory "glass headgear,"[43] "diving helmet,"[44] and "helmet with a glass section in front of the face."[45] It seems clear that these helmets are not intended merely to protect against mechanical damage. Some details noticed by a witness in Argentina strongly imply that the helmet was worn to isolate the owner from the atmosphere. A typical dwarf came out of a large, egg-shapped object wearing a helmet that was linked to the object by three cables.[46] This arrangement sounds very much like umbilical connections between a space suit and a life-support system, a concept that was not prevalent in Argentina at the time of this sighting in 1965. One cannot escape concluding that these individuals could not breathe the earth's atmosphere, or that they chose not to.

No such restriction applies generally to the UFO people, however, because neither helmets nor other breathing equipment were seen in the majority of the sightings. Most of the UFO people of both races appear to be perfectly comfortable breathing the air. This dilemma demands a set of circumstances consistent with the observations about wearing helmets; that is, some do, some don't.

The most significant aspect of this data is that large numbers of the UFO people can and do breathe the air. There can be no doubt that their biological system is based upon metabolism of oxygen, since no other atmospheric gas can serve this function. Their life energy must depend upon consumption of oxygen obtained through breathing combined with the chemical degradation of foods, in the manner of humans. Furthermore, the atmosphere that they are accustomed to breathing must contain oxygen, and the amount cannot be greatly different than on earth.

To pursue this inquiry further requires some technical details about gas mixtures and respiration. The oxygen content of air is about 21% based upon dry volume, and that proportion remains nearly constant at all altitudes up to about 25 miles. But the proportion of oxygen is not directly related to breathing. Man lives comfortably at sea level, but he cannot survive above 25,000 ft without supplemental oxygen. The molecular concentration of oxygen, or the pressure exerted by oxygen alone, at the higher altitudes becomes insufficient to transfer oxygen to the blood in the lungs. The important parameter that indicates the suitability for breathing is the partial pressure of oxygen. At sea level it is 159 mm Hg. The minimum viable value for man is about 69 mm Hg. But there is no upper limit; man can breathe pure oxygen.

Although the UFO people have been seen wearing helmets that suggest a special gas mixture for respiration, there is no need to assume that they were compelled to do so. As pilots of craft that fly to extreme altitudes, they might habitually wear helmets and, in a few landings, merely fail to take them off. Simply seeing the helmets does not necessarily mean that the UFO people would be uncomfortable or possibly imperiled by breathing air. They could be accustomed to an atmosphere that is identical or very similar to that on earth. But many other explanations are possible.

Let it be supposed that the helmets are intended to supply a special mixture of gases and, for the moment, explore the implications concerning only one gas, oxygen. If the partial pressure of oxygen that these people customarily breathe were *less* than on earth and their range of oxygen tolerance were comparable to man, then they should not have any difficulty in breathing ordinary air, relatively rich in oxygen for them, and helmets should not be required. On the other hand, if the partial pressure of oxygen in their native atmosphere were *greater*, than on earth, a distinct need for the helmets might arise. The difference would have to be substantial, say, by a factor of two or three times greater, before they would experience difficulty. Being acclimated to an oxygen-rich atmosphere, they would find the oxygen-poor atmosphere on earth to be troublesome. Helmets would be in order for extended exploration outside the craft; however, shorter excursions might be undertaken without them. In time, they might become adjusted to the earth's atmosphere and no longer need the helmets. For their native atmosphere to have a partial pressure of oxygen vastly greater than on earth is out of the question because they would then never be seen *sans* helmets. It appears that a native atmosphere containing oxygen at a partial pressure somewhat higher than on earth is at least compatible with the observations.

Unfortunately, this line of inquiry conflicts with another forceful implication of the data. As the dwarves are sometimes reported to have abnormally large chests,[47] they may have adapted to low concentrations of oxygen in their homeland as have the South American Indians who live in the Andean highlands.[48] It may be worth noting that this adaptation in South America has occurred in a short period of time compared to the millions of years usually associated with evolutionary changes. The penetration of *homo sapiens* into the Western hemisphere was initiated by Mongoloid people crossing the Bering Sea from Asia to North America about 11,500 years ago. They and their progeny spread gradually southward across the continent, reaching the northern portions of South America in a period of about 700 years, or about 10,800 years ago[49] If a certain fraction of these people having abnormally large chests preferentially sought out the mountain habitat and others did not, eons of time may have been taken in developing the chest. It seems much more reasonable to postulate that a typical group of immigrants by chance, found the mountains to their liking and settled there. In this case, the maximum time available for the adaptation to be achieved was only 10,800 years. Even less time would have been involved if the people first saturated more favorable locations before moving into the highlands by choice or when fleeing from the victors in tribal warfare.

One wonders if the sighting reports contain any clues that would aid in estimating the total atmospheric pressure in the homeland of the UFO people. Helmets might be used as part of a space suit to prevent caisson disease, also known as the bends, if their native pressure were much lower than the atmosphere on earth. A serious medical hazard arises when a person is exposed to nitrogen under increased pressure for an extended period. The blood absorbs more nitrogen than usual and, if decompression proceeds too rapidly, the blood releases it in the form of bubbles. To avoid distressing symptoms or death, the individual must be returned to his normal pressure in slow and controlled stages, allowing the excess nitrogen in the blood to be expelled gradually by the lungs. If the UFO people were accustomed to an atmosphere in which the pressure of nitrogen were much lower than on earth, one would rarely observe them without their helmets.

On the other hand, a native pressure considerably higher than one atmosphere would also require the use of a helmet but here the question reverts back to an adequate supply of oxygen as already discussed.

In summary, wearing of helmets on earth is not usually required and they may be worn more from personal preference than from necessity. The native atmosphere certainly contains oxygen but the available information is too sketchy to establish its partial pressure relative to that on earth. Neither can the total pressure be deduced. However, the partial pressure of oxygen and the total pressure cannot be greatly different from 159 mm Hg and 14.7 psi, respectively.

Boots and Gloves

Footwear is seldom noted but two types have been recognized, namely, ordinary boots and a heelless shoe that is integral with the trousers, such as childrens' "pajamas-with-the-feet-in-'em." A robot-like being associated with a UFO was seen in Florida wearing thin, white gloves but the report does not suggest why.[50]

*Every great advance in science
has issued from a new audacity
of imagination.*

— *John Dewey*

CHAPTER 9

ACTIVITIES ON EARTH

As the UFO people have said that they are conducting a scientific investigation on earth, one would expect that they have been observed in the process. A thorough study of earth would require an enormous variety of activities. Concerning the natural environment, it would be necessary to collect and analyze all sorts of samples, including plants and animals, rocks and soils, water, and the atmosphere. Some instrumental measurements, such as gravity, magnetism, geological substructure, and radioactivity, would be required. Finally, man-made installations of particular interest would be inspected and samples of industrial products would be collected.

Collecting Samples

Considerable interest in plants, both natural and cultivated, has been displayed. In France, two dwarves examined lavender plants being grown commercially for their fragrance.[1] Tomato plants attracted the attention of two others in Brazil,[2] whereas some associates on another occasion collected tobacco plants.[3] More enterprising and better organized efforts in Portugal in-

volved gathering "flowers, shrubs, and twigs in a shiny box."[4]
"Grass, herbs, and leaves of trees" were the target for three little
men in Brazil.[5] "With smiles showing fine white teeth," two
dwarves took a pot of flowers from an Italian woman.[6] Other
instances are less explicit: "they gathered some plants," "picked
up something," etc.

A Brazilian prospector saw two dwarves "digging a hole."[7]
Two more were seen by a dairy farmer in New York, each
carrying a tray of "what appeared to be soil removed from the
field."[8] In Venezuela, stones were picked up and examined,[9] and
in another instance, two dwarves leaped into a spherical craft
"carrying stones and other samples."[10]

Among various kinds of animals reportedly taken aboard UFOs
are a chicken,[11] and, over the objection of the owner, some
domestic rabbits.[12] Attempts at acquiring dogs have met with
some difficulty. Frisky, a dog owned by a 12-year-old boy, was
seen in a field with other dogs near a UFO and four normal-
looking people, two men and two women. Frisky growled and
backed away when one of the men tried to grab him. The man
then attempted to catch one of the other dogs, but let go when he
was bitten.[13] Another dog owner was rather abusive when a dwarf
asked him for his pet. The dwarf was sent fleeing back into his
craft with "Get the hell out of here."[14]

In areas where UFOs have been active for several days, it is
commonly reported that many farm animals, including cattle, are
missing. The residents usually attribute their losses to the UFOs
without any direct evidence of theft. A newspaper in Rio de
Janeiro and local papers at Manaus, in the State of Amazonas, on
September 18, 1962, carried reports that flying saucers had
carried off seventeen chickens, six pigs, and two cows from the
Barcelos district. Proof of this pudding, however, occurred near
Twin Falls, Idaho, where the victims watched the culprits. People
from a UFO were seen loading a steer into their machine, which
was estimated to be 200 feet in diameter. The witnesses were a
local attorney, the ranch owner, and two hired hands.[15]

Most, if not all, of these instances of collecting samples are at least compatible with the notion of an objective study. But some of the items taken by the dwarves may relate to their personal need; that is, fresh food. chicken gumbo, fried rabbit, or steak might be a delectable change to a diet of cookies "made of corn and wheat flour" plus other ingredients that were observed being cooked on a UFO. The witness obtained four of the cookies which were later tested, eaten, and analyzed.[16]

Collection of water has been reported frequently. It would be adequate to take small samples of water in a vial for determination of the dissolved minerals and the level of pollution, either chemical or bacterial. UFO people, however, sometimes take substantial amounts of water. A Canadian and his wife in 1950 saw a large UFO with portholes "come to rest on the suface of the lake." Ten small people on a deck busily "immersed a hose in the lake" as if pumping water into the craft.[17] An almost identical performance, also in Canada, had been observed 36 years earlier when eight witnesses saw dwarves plunging a hose into a lake from a spherical craft resting on the water.[18] While fishing in New York, an electronics engineer saw an object land. Two dwarves "came out with a hose and pumped water from the river."[19] Another fisherman in Italy saw a UFO hover for 10 minutes over a river with "a hose that plunged into the water."[20] These uses of hoses imply collection of a substantial volume of water, probably more than could be carried in buckets on several round trips. Any such amount would clearly exceed the immediate requirements of the collectors, and one suspects that it filled the need of a considerable number of their fellows somewhere else.

The intended purpose for water, on one occasion, was made entirely clear to a chicken farmer in Wisconsin. An object came down vertically near his house in which he saw three men through an open hatch. One of them handed him a "silvery jug with two handles" and "made a motion like drinking." The jug was filled with water and returned.[21] This case is reminiscent of a previously mentioned request for water by a strange woman in Brazil who used the word, "Rempaua."[22] In yet another instance, two fair-skinned men emerged from a UFO in Chile asking a miner for water in a "mixture of English and Spanish." With unusual resourcefulness under the circumstances, the miner took some water out of his car radiator and gave it to them.[23] Small quantities of water were also obtained by the UFO people without assistance from humans. Two miners saw a UFO land on a sandbar in a California river. One dwarf got out and "filled a shiny pail with water and handed it to someone inside the craft."[24] Another craft landed at night near a Brazilian fisherman who watched one of three little men fill a "shiny metal tube with water from the river."[25]

Notwithstanding the declared purpose of the UFO people, these instances of collecting water, with one possible exception, have a distinctively unscientific tone. It appears that water is required for drinking, or other purposes, either by the individuals involved or a number of their colleagues. In view of the normally furtive behavior of these people, a face-to-face confrontation to request water carries a hint of some desperation.

Their interest in manufactured products seems to be minimal. A railroad worker was surprised when a strange being entered the sleeping coach where he was reading. After "pouring the contents of an oil can into a small bottle," he left.[26] This visitor apparently needed some oil rather urgently. The only other instance concerning a manufactured product occurred when two small men associated with a UFO were discussing agriculture with a farmer in New York. At their request, the farmer went to get some fertilizer, but upon returning, found that they had gone. He left the fertilizer. It, too, was gone the next day.[27]

Inspections

Somewhat more attention has been paid to a variety of man-made structures. Very commonly UFOs and their occupants have been observed in the vicinity of highways and railroads. These may only be convenient places to land, but a specific curiosity has been exhibited. For example, three dwarves were seen looking at railroad tracks with a light in the early morning hours.[28] Abandoned oil derricks in Texas attracted the attention of a figure about 1 meter tall who emerged from a huge UFO.[29] An object fitting the description of a UFO was seen on the ground near the site of the first A-bomb explosion in New Mexico, although no occupants were discerned.[30]

Dispersal of an array of apparatus on the ground near a landed UFO and diligent work with some kind of equipment would suggest scientific data gathering. Only two instances might be understood in this context. Human figures came out of an egg-shaped object in Ohio and "placed small spheres around the craft."[31] Perhaps the same type of device was involved in the appearance of a man in Argentina who held a "pale blue sphere in his hand."[32]

In summary, the idea that the UFO people are conducting any kind of organized and thorough scientific study on earth is not sustained by the available information. Instead, their activities on the ground are strangely haphazard and disorganized. Aside from the collection of vegetables, small animals, and water, possibly for consumption, other samples seem to be selected at random. Also, inspection of man-made facilities seems to be more a matter of curiosity than an organized study. Instead of conducting a comprehensive survey of earth, the UFO people appear to be randomly snooping around or searching for some particular, natural commodity on earth, either vegetable or mineral.

Emergencies

Sometimes the observed activities are not related to investigation of the surroundings because the visitors' attention is focused upon the craft itself. In January 1967, a UFO about 80 ft in diameter settled on its tripod landing gear on a highway in Minnesota. From an elevator descended from the underside, a man wearing blue coveralls and a glass helmet stepped out. "He seemed to check something" before leaving.[33] Similar inspections were observed in France,[34] San Salvador,[35] Argentina[36] and Minnesota.[37] Taking advantage of a landing in Brazil to check their vehicle, the pilots also investigated the area and "gathered samples in a huge box."[38] Actual repairs were sometimes required. A French woman, approaching to within 30 meters of a landed disc, stated "that a man was repairing it."[39] External repairs were also made on vehicles that landed in Minnesota[40] and Denmark.[41]

Maintenance or adjustment of equipment inside a craft may also require a landing. After touching a landed machine, a Libyan farmer was warned with gestures by one of its occupants to stay away. He watched for 20 minutes as six men inside were "apparently busy with instruments."[42] Of course, they may have been taking some kind of measurements, but such interpretation seems unlikely in view of the following incident. One of two UFOs flying at low altitude settled to the ground near an amateur prospector in a remote area of Canada. He sat quietly for 20 to 30 minutes sketching the object but seeing no activity. Then, as a door opened, he smelled an odor like "a burned-out electrical motor."[43] Because the odor clearly came from inside the craft, it appears that the landing was forced to correct a malfunction of electrical machinery or circuitry, or to put out a fire. In two instances, figures inside their vehicle were observed to be busy with electrical apparatus. A man outside a landed machine in Argentina was studying a piece of paper while a companion inside was "seated before an instrument panel."[44] Three figures stood on a platform under a landed UFO in Brazil, apparently guarding the vehicle as they were armed, while another was seen through a transparent top seemingly "using a keyboard."[45]

In other words, some landings occur in which the occupants display no interest in their surroundings. The purpose of the landing seems to be inspection of parts outside the vehicle and making necessary repairs. Alternately, complete attention is focused upon instrument panels and control boards within the vehicle. This group of cases appear to be emergency landings to fix something that either malfunctioned or threatened to fail. While UFOs clearly represent an advanced technology, they apparently are not foolproof. In a large number of missions, therefore, one would expect that occasionally the necessary repairs could not be accomplished and the UFO would have to be abandoned on the ground. Or, an equipment failure in flight would result in disintegration of the craft or a devastating crash on the ground. The record indicates that both types of mishaps have occurred.

A UFO in Brazil, flying at low altitude with serious difficulty, suddenly pulled up, whereupon it "disintegrated into thousands of fiery fragments, which fell sparkling with magnificent brightness." Some of the fragments, extinguished in shallow water, were later determined to be magnesium.[46] In 1952, wreckage of a UFO was found on Spitzbergen Island in the Arctic Ocean. Investigation was conducted by a Norwegian Board of Inquiry, which later announced: "It has—this we wish to state emphatically—not been built by any country on earth."[47] Both these incidents were studied by the Condon Committee and neatly, but dubiously, dispatched. Three more UFO crashes in the American deserts were described in 1950. One of these involved a saucer-shaped craft 100 ft in diameter in which 16 little people were killed. Their heights ranged from "about 36 to 42 inches."[48] These reports have never been adequately investigated and described publicly because the vehicles and the bodies were reportedly commandeered by the Air Force.

Personnel Transfers

An effective method of secretly investigating a limited area would be for a UFO to land at night, discharge a reconnaissance team, then fly away. Upon completing their mission, the team would signal for a pickup or meet the craft at some prearranged location and time. Something like this was apparently in process when a guard in New York saw a cigar-shaped machine land in a parking lot one evening at 10:15 p.m. While he was watching the object in the beam of his truck headlights, two dwarves dressed in "shiny black uniforms" ran out of the darkness and entered the craft, which took off immediately. Black uniforms seem to be singularly appropriate for a surreptitious outing at night.[49] Obviously two crafts would have to land together for an occupant of one of them to transfer to the other. Just such a situation was observed in Central Australia by a group of Unmatjera aborigines in 1951. They were looking at a UFO on the ground when another one like it landed nearby. A dwarf came from under the late arrival, ran over to the parked craft, and climbed aboard through the bottom.[50] Three years later in France, several witnesses even saw a double transfer. Two discs in the sky with a "sort of luminous bridge between them" were seen to land together. One dwarf came out of both vehicles, passing each other without hesitation, to enter the opposite craft. Then both flew away.[51] These little dramas unfortunately give no clues as to why the transfers were made, but they clearly identify another purpose for UFO landings.

Summary on Landings

As with many other inquiries, the eventual answer turns out to be more complex than was initially suspected. So it was with the reasons that UFOs abandon the safety of the skies to hover close to the ground or actually land. Reports by witnesses clearly indicate that landings are most frequently associated with investigation of the surroundings by the UFO people. They often collect samples of a wide variety, but in a seemingly unsystematic way. An undefined need for water in quantities ranging from approximately one quart to hundreds of gallons brought several UFOs to the ground, and under conditons of urgency, human assistance was solicited. Malfunction of propulsion or control systems has evidently forced landings for inspections and repairs. Discharging or picking up passengers and transferring individuals between UFOs is sometimes required. One further purpose for landing, related to investigation of humans, is treated in the next section.

Infiltration

From the foregoing discussion it is suspected that UFO people of average height would have little difficulty in infiltrating modern society. They are obviously capable of breathing the earth's atmosphere and they could not be distinguished in a crowd by their appearance. Of course, they would benefit by being fluent in an appropriate language and they would have to wear common styles of clothing. In a well-planned mission, one or several of them could be landed in the middle of the night, not too far from a populated area, walk into town, and blend completely with the population on the sidewalks. Provided with adequate funds, they could establish residences, take jobs, and become an undifferentiated element of the society. A handsome young man named Valiant Thor claims that he came to earth in a space ship and was "landed in a clearing just north of High Bridge, New Jersey." Thereafter he mingled in a small crowd at a convention. He said that his mission, lasting three years, was to educate government leaders. He's not around anymore.[52]

Personal Locomotion

Every species of animal has a distinctive carriage of its body and a typical way of moving its limbs when walking or running. While the difference between species may be very slight, they are easily discerned. Even individual members within a species have a style of movement that can be identified. One can usually recognize a friend at great distance by that characteristic alone. Thus a close examination of the movements of the UFO people should be sensitive to any such peculiarities mentioned by the witnesses.

Weak Gravity

Most accounts of the UFO people indicate that they were moving about in an ordinary way as they walked near their craft, picked up something, or ran back to the craft and climbed aboard. Somewhat unusual movements, however, were displayed in France in 1957 by four dwarves who had a waddling gait.[53] That same type of movement was undoubtedly observed by a farm woman in Peru, who described six dwarves that "walked like ducks."[54] Because of the multiplicity of dwarves in both of these cases, the observations must be taken as characteristic of the species rather than idiosyncratic. Other strange styles of walking included jerky motions,[55] stiff-legged,[56] and with feet together in a series of jumps.[57] One is struck by the similarity between these descriptions and the odd gaits adopted by the Apollo astronauts as they walked about on the lunar surface. Anyone who watched the television broadcasts will recall how they bounded forward in a series of galloping jumps, turned by twisting their torsos, and cavorted about with childlike movements. The implication is that UFO people are similarly experiencing a gravity on earth less than they are accustomed to; this point is emphatic in a few reports. A professor in Brazil noted that upon re-entering their craft, two men of average height jumped up the stairway lightly, holding only by one hand, whereas he had to use both hands when he followed them.[58] Two dwarves in Venezuela came out of the bushes with their arms full of what appeared to be earth or rocks, and they leaped with great ease into a luminous sphere hovering six feet above the ground.[59] A truly impressive and significant performance was seen by a Brazilian survey worker, who watched for half an hour as three 7-foot-tall beings, with extraordinary agility, leaped, gambolled, and tossed huge stones before boarding their craft.[60]

The argument that the UFO people have a home somewhere on earth has not been very convincing[61] and the only alternative, for physically real beings, is that their home is somewhere else. Exactly where is not known, but that issue is probed in another chapter. The point here is limited to considering gravity. Relative to the gravitational strength on earth, taken as 1.0g, the surface gravity of planets in our solar system varies rather widely from a minimum of 0.27g on Mercury to a maximum of 2.64g on Jupiter. Only three of the nine planets have gravity within 20% of that on earth.[62] The gravitational field in the astronomical homeland of the UFO people, whether in this solar system or some other is not likely to be the same as on earth, or even very close to it. Through the space program, the human body has been found to be surprisingly tolerant to extremes of gravity or the forces of acceleration that are equivalent. On lunar flights, the astronauts must sustain the short-term accelerations during rocket burns, the long-term weightlessness in earth or lunar orbit and enroute to the moon, the weak gravity of 1.6g while exploring the lunar surface or resting in the Lunar Excursion Module. If adequately supported in a semi-reclining position, the astronauts can even endure the forces of re-entering the earth's atmosphere, amounting to 8 to 10g, without unacceptable loss of mental, visual, or manual ability. But walking, struggling to stay upright, in a strong gravitational field is another matter. It should be possible for a man to walk in a field of 2g, where his weight would be twice normal. It would require great strength, and the extra exertion would tire him quickly. In 3g, it is doubtful that he could do any more than crawl around very laboriously, if at all. Consequently, man will not be exploring heavenly bodies where the gravity is much greater than on earth without some mechanical reinforcement of his limbs and an auxiliary power source, a concept that has been under active development for many years. Exporation of planets and satellites having lesser gravity, however, is relatively easy and apparently enjoyable. As these considerations should apply equally to residents of other worlds that wished to explore the cosmos, the odds are that their target planets would have relatively weaker gravity. In all probability, gravity in the homeland of the UFO people is substantially greater than 1g, as attested by their agility on earth and their lack of special equipment for walking.

Creatures of nature proliferate in nearly infinite forms, each finding a narrow ledge of existence that provides an adequate food supply and suitable living conditions. Despite the enormous variety, they are all governed by the environmental factors dictated by nature, such as temperature, pressure, light, and gravity, which is of special interest here. What kind of creatures and plants, would live on earth if its gravity were only one-fourth the present strength? Or four times the present strength? Some differences would certainly be noted. But judging from the happy existence on earth of creatures of all sizes from the ant to the elephant, the strength of gravity does not severely limit the size of living things. It governs their bodily proportions in relation to their total weight. This point can be understood most readily in the context of plants and trees. A tree trunk, for example, must be strong enough to support the total weight of the tree. It must also resist structural failure in buckling, that is, bending outward at the middle, then collapsing. This same concept applies to the limbs of animals, which must be even stronger and more rigid. Larger creatures are required by gravity to have relatively sturdier limbs. The cross-section must be greater in proportion to the length, as for elephants compared to ants. This relationship would be intensified for stronger gravity and mollified for weaker. Hence, the bodily forms of the UFO people should contain a clue to the gravity of their homeland if it were different than that on earth. These creatures, spanning the considerable range of heights from about 0.5 to 3.0 meters, are uniformly judged to be skinny by human standards. This observation implies that their native gravity is less than that on earth. As many other ramifications are involved, no definite conclusion is possible. Not only is the sturdiness of animal limbs controlled by gravity, but so is nearly every other aspect of their existence, such as metabolic rate, surface area, respiration frequency, and heart rate. These quantities, expressible in mathematical form, are related to the prevailing gravity.[63] A thin body form could also be an advantage in disposing of heat in a warm climate. Clearly, a great deal of effort is required to clarify this subject.

Flying

Upon first exposure to the UFO literature, the reader is prone to ignore any reference to the dwarves seen hovering or flying through the air, or to dismiss the story as totally beyond the UFO phenomenon. Maintaining a mental tranquility during extensive reading, however, is not so easy. In the sample cases under study, the UFO people were reportedly flying on numerous occasions, and these events must be objectively examined.

A man in Venezuela saw an object in flight that landed near a bridge. He first thought it was a heron, but then saw that it was a little man with all the characteristics of the UFO dwarves.[64] Upon being awakened by the shaking of his bed, another witness saw a small creature fly out an open window toward a dazzling light.[65] When a dwarf was disturbed by a racetrack employee while attacking a horse in a barn, he "zoomed" out the door.[66] These strange observations standing alone might be disregarded in the absence of the following ones, which specifically link the flying creatures to UFOs.

The normal way that UFO people enter their craft is through a hatch or doorway in the side, by stepping into an elevator that has been let down from a hovering craft, or by climbing up a stairway on the underside. If it is too high or they are in a great hurry, they simply fly to it. A small creature dressed in shiny clothes seemed to "fly" as he moved toward a craft hovering less than 2 meters above the ground. It "opened up" and the creature "popped inside."[67] Two creatures in white suits and helmets were seen in Canada to fly back into a large disc-shaped craft.[68] Two children in France saw "four little devils" that hovered, flew around a 2-meter sphere, then dived into it.[69] Only two days later in Venezuela with little chance of communication, a police officer saw a dwarf wearing a silver-colored, metallic-looking coverall. The dwarf lifted one foot, then the other, and flew up toward an object overhead and sailed into an open door.[70] The prominence of clothing in these cases should be noted.

While these observations are truly baffling, they are elementary compared to the next two that, oddly enough, furnish a clue to comprehension. A twenty-three-year-old woman and her parents saw a strange little man surrounded by a bluish-yellow glow as he soared over the neighbors rooftops.[71] Here is a direct association between flying and luminosity. The same relationship was reported for the taller UFO people when a strange being 2.10-m tall was seen hovering in the air near a bright object; his body emitted a peculiar glow.[72] The bodies of two dwarves appeared to glow with lights of changing colors as they emerged from a landed vehicle in New York.[73] The idea that the bodies were emitting light has probably been confused by the witnesses with luminescence of the clothing and the atmosphere surrounding the creatures. Three giants, 3 meters tall, wore luminous clothing as they came out of a huge machine over 10 stories high.[74] A minister in Ohio saw a silhouette wearing a luminous suit near his house.[75] A man 2.5 m tall wore luminous heelless boots as he inspected his craft in San Salvador.[76] The aerial activity of luminous bodies and changing colors sounds all too familiar; it closely parallels the emission of light from UFOs in flight. Apparently, the type of propulsion system used by these people for personal flying is the same as that employed to drive their vehicles. It would seem that the "shiny" quality of their clothing, the sheen or the radiance, is a necessary adjunct to the system, making the clothing most unusual and possibly explaining the lack of buttons, fasteners, and seams. With some kind of electromagnetic system involving the surface of the clothing, the discontinuities created by fasteners and seams would be undesirable. A gap between trouser cuffs and shoes seems to be avoided by making the shoes integral with the standard coveralls. Similar care to preserve extraordinary smoothness also applies to the surface of the vehicles.

Some other aspect of flying may have been involved in two isolated observations. Two boys in Brazil, ages 9 and 11, saw a luminous sphere at treetop level from which descended a tall being gliding down to the ground along two vertical beams of light. Since strong beams are frequently aimed downward from UFOs, they could have been extraneous to the descent for the being flew back up to the sphere without their benefit.[77] A more distinct indication that the light beams were important occurred in Venezuela about three years later. Two beings came out of an oval object through a system of light beams, and they returned to their craft "as if carried by the light."[78] Two men skiing through the woods near Helsinki furnished a very detailed description of this process.[79] Thus the aerial performance of at least three of the UFO people probably encompasses a use of light beams that is entirely unique.

In the previous section, it was observed that the UFO people did not wear special equipment to protect their bodies against strong gravity. This point was used to argue that they did not need it because they came from someplace where gravity was greater than on earth. It now becomes clear, however, that their remarkable clothing could well serve as a device to relieve the body of burdensome gravitational forces. If it is capable of offsetting the body weight entirely for the purpose of flying, it could also serve to offset any desired fraction of the body weight to facilitate walking in an abnormally high gravity. Numerous examples of the UFO people being seen as brightly luminous while walking on the ground, instead of flying, are ample indication of that usage. One very small creature was even seen quietly walking the streets of Chaclacay, Peru, leaving a luminous trail, a feature commonly associated with the vehicles and understandable in that context.[80] It appears that the clothing furnishes protection against gravity, and on that basis, the argument becomes admissible that the UFO people originate in gravity that is less than that on earth.

Attitudes Toward Humanity

With very minor exceptions, the UFO people clearly refrain from interfering in human affairs, even to the extent of evading detection. Avoidance of continental land masses and islands may be inferred from the frequency with which UFOs are seen to appear from the direction of the sea and to depart toward the sea. Considering the limited number of people traveling upon the oceans at any given instant, it is surprising that they have generated so many reports. Numerous observations of UFOs entering the oceans or erupting therefrom amidst great turbulence and then flying off have been collected and analyzed. In 1945, for example, crew members on the U.S. Army Transport Delarof were steaming toward Seattle in the northeastern Pacific. A large, round object, estimated to be 150 to 250 ft in diameter, emerged from the sea, circled the ship two or three times, then flew off toward the south.[81] Similarly, an object off the coast of Italy caused an enormous bubble in the sea 1 kilometer from a boat carrying four people: it emerged, hovered briefly, and flew away at high speed.[82] Such events have also been observed in relation to numerous rivers and lakes. It is not known why UFOs frequent the waters of the earth, but while submerged in them they are certainly well hidden from mankind.

Most sightings merely involve metallic, disc-shaped craft traversing the sky with strange, jerky motions during the day, or the corresponding behavior of a bright light at night. To see a UFO at close range, hovering at low altitude, or resting on the ground is a rare event. Reliable statistics are not available, but the relative frequency of landings versus flybys can be crudely assessed. It has been estimated by a Gallup poll that five million Americans are convinced that they have seen UFOs. If only a modest fraction of this number were valid, the total number of sightings worldwide must still be quite large, say, on the order of 50,000,000! As for landings and near-landings, on the other hand, only about 1,000 have been documented, and it is not known how many observations may have gone unrecorded or how many landings went unobserved. The indication of rarity is clear, and based upon the very sketchy data at hand, one might place the landing-to-flyby ratio on the order of 1 in 10,000. No matter what the correct figures may be, the objectives of the UFO people seem to be largely achieved without landing.

And to make things worse, even these rare events take place almost exclusively at night. The frequency of short-range sightings rises quickly to a peak about one hour after sunset; sightings later in the evening and throughout the night decline as potential witnesses go to bed.[83] But this pattern of landings may be significant in another way. During the evening twilight, the brightness of direct sunlight is relieved, yet the level of general illumination is quite high enough for good visibility. It is possible that the UFO people dislike, or cannot tolerate, broad daylight, or any bright light for that matter. A few observations lend support to this idea. A policeman in Chalac, Argentina, along with about 50 Toba Indians, saw three little men getting out of a UFO. One of the witnesses started taking flash pictures of them and noticed that they were afraid of the bright light.[84] In California, a robot-like creature tried all night to dislodge a hunter from a tree in which he had taken refuge. The creature was kept at bay by the witness, who set fire to fragments of his clothing and threw them at his tormenter.[85] An attempted abduction in Brazil was frustrated because the witness noticed that the three 7-ft-tall people trying to catch him shunned bright sunlight.[86] From such flimsy data it is not possible to draw conclusions, but the suggestion is evident that the UFO people prefer to land after sunset because they are, like owls, bedazzled by ordinary daylight. Most animal eyes can accommodate to very low levels of light, but they are sharply limited in their capacity to block out excessive brightness. The reluctance of the UFO people to expose themselves to bright light implies that they are accustomed to levels that may be very much weaker than daylight on earth. This prospect may explain why the dwarves have notably large, bulging eyes, and why some witnesses insist that they appear to have a reddish glow at night, like nocturnal animals.[87] Sunglasses, of course would be the simple answer to this problem, but they are not used. On the other hand, helmets made of tinted glass would serve very well. They would be highly reflective from the outside and would make it difficult for the witness to observe facial details of the wearer as is sometimes the case. It is not known whether the UFO people wear helmets more frequently when the illumination is high than in the dark of night.

It has also been shown that landings in France during a wave of activity in 1954 were correlated with areas of low population density.[88] In other words, the UFOs tended to avoid metropolitan areas in favor of farmlands or more isolated swamps and woodlands, a propensity that is also observed in other countries. It is remarkable under the circumstances that any detailed information is available concerning the behavior of UFO people on the ground, but there is enough data to verify their aloofness and to decipher something of their motives.

The typical, close-up sighting consists of the following stages:

1) The witness sees a UFO at considerable altitude and watches it approach, hover, and land nearby,
2) One or more occupants emerges,
3) They deliberately engage in some activity,
4) They complete the work and reboard the craft, and
5) The UFO takes off.

Roughly half of the sightings involving occupants followed this pattern to the letter. Such a consistent format implies that the UFO people selected a landing place where it was thought that they would not be observed. They proceeded to carry out their mission under the false impression and took no action to discover if they were being watched. These data might be understood to mean that the UFO people did not care whether they were being watched or not. This explanation, however, is untenable on the basis of the predominant isolation of landing sites. Nearly identical sequences occurred in many other cases, but with minor variations. The witness failed, for example, to see the actual landing, so the episode started at Stage 2; or the craft was hidden from view behind trees, thus preventing the observation of Stages 2 and 4. These variations strengthen rather than alter the conclusion that the UFO people deliberately sought to carry out a mission unobserved and thought that it had been so accomplished. Their presence and activities on earth were intended to be secret.

It is among the exceptions to the above, when an interaction takes place between the UFO people and the witnesses, that meaningful behavior patterns may be observed. Witnesses rarely say anything about facial expressions, which seem to be uniformly blank, although a few smiles have been evoked.[89] An English woman reported seeing two men looking out a hovering craft "sternly, not in an unkind fashion, but almost sadly, compassionately.''[90] To a farm woman in Pennsylvania, the appearance of a man in a UFO seemed to be "quizzical."[91] Clearly, little regarding the attitude of the UFO people is to be gleaned from their facial expressions. With hardly any display of normal human warmth, the UFO people sometimes wave or make perplexing gestures[92] that are rarely interpreted as threatening,[93] or, in passing, they say something to the witness that is usually not understood.[94] The UFO people do not behave as though they feared humans. On the contrary, it is the witnesses that flee in panic.[95] An Italian saw a UFO from which emerged two men wearing yellow coveralls and wide belts. Upon noticing that the witness was afraid, one of them made a reassuring gesture before they departed.[96] Very generally, one might say that the UFO people are furtive, seldom display any emotion, and have a kindly but restrained disposition.

As occasional acts of agression seem to be more in self-defense than from an innate hostility, any resulting injuries to the witnesses should probably be judged as accidental. An 18-year-old boy in Venezuela was paralyzed by a weapon when he discovered six dwarves loading stones into a UFO.[97] Such paralysis does not cause injury and it is usually quite temporary, lasting just long enough for the intruders to escape. But it may last for some time. When a French farmer surprised two dwarves who were examining a plant, he was immobilized when they aimed a small device at him. He was left alone in his field for 20 minutes, unable to move or call for help. And, as one would expect, he was thoroughly frightened.[98] The effect upon the nervous system of the weapons used in these attacks is unique: they usually inhibit voluntary control of the muscles without interfering with the involuntary body processes, or without rendering the victim unconscious.

Loss of consciousness, however, is sometimes induced by the weapon. A strange man in Illinois stunned witnesses by pointing a device at them that "made consciousness dissolve."[99] Upon approaching to within 2 meters of a large UFO in the Everglades, a hunter was knocked unconscious for 24 hours by a ray that struck him on the forehead. Upon awakening, he had lost sight in the right eye, saw poorly with the left, and had to be hospitalized for 5 days.[100] Other symptoms reported by victims of such attacks are electric shock,[101] burns,[102] physical displacement,[103] and headache.[104]

Two or three types of weapons can be identified in 18 cases in which they were seen but not always used. Most prominent is a small metal tube that, from the brief descriptions, one judges to be slightly larger than a ballpoint pen. A larger device is similar to a 2-cell flashlight. Finally, a small flashing box also seems to be a weapon. In most instances, the UFO people were merely seen carrying this box[105] but one witness seems to have been injured by a figure armed with it.[106] A woman in luminous clothing standing beside a UFO in New York seemed to be well armed with a tube in one hand and a box in the other although she fired neither.[107]

A curious aspect of the weapons is that they eject a beam of light that is seen by the witnesses and reported to be a definite color, such as green,[108] blue,[109] violet,[110] and red,[111] or sometimes merely bright[112] or blinding.[113] The data are not sufficient to establish a correlation between the color of the light ray and its effect upon the witness, although the only two records of red rays and red balls of light both resulted in burning the witnesses.[114] And it is not possible to discover which effects upon the witnesses are produced by which weapons. A further implication that cannot be explored is that the intensity of the beam is variable at will and produces a greater or lesser effect upon the victim. All this discussion about ray guns "zapping" their targets into immobility sounds like science fiction. The witnesses, however, were serious and the last thing one does in a hoax is to injure himself. It would be most valuable to discover the exact nature of these weapons, for their use by law enforcement agencies would be extremely effective and humane. Actually, such a weapon may already have been developed. "Operation Zeke" was reportedly organized by the Federal Aviation Agency under the direction of Dr. H. L. Reighard to counter the epidemic of airplanes being hijacked to Cuba in the late sixties. A device based upon high-frequency radiation was developed that would instantly knock the victim unconscious; a hijacker between two ray boxes "would wake up wondering what happened to him." These devices were never used because of uncertainties and danger in the event of two hihackers on a plane.[115] This research should be brought into the open and completed so that society can benefit from the improved security that such weapons would provide.

In a famous case in New Jersey, a man and his wife were captured and taken aboard a UFO against their will for about two hours for the purpose of some biomedical experiments.[116] A young man in Brazil was also captured after a valiant struggle and taken aboard a UFO for a medical examination. In a period of two hours, he was also seduced by a strangely attractive woman, twice.[117] The implied meaning of this case is that the UFO people, being genetically compatible with humans, are themselves thoroughly human. It could be that they and humanity share a common ancestry, or that one group descended from the other. Which relationship is correct and how it occurred extends too far beyond the scope of this book for further comment here. Other attempts at capturing humans have failed[118] and actual abductions may have been witnessed by others.[119] The literature, of course, contains no reports from people that may have been spirited away permanently.

The UFO people are well aware of humanity, but with few exceptions, they do not wish to establish direct, friendly relationships. They prefer to conduct their activities on earth in secret, taking considerable care to avoid being seen. They will defend themselves if need be, but they intend no harm to mankind, even though for short-term experiments they will capture specimens.

> *In the light of recent developments, the situation has reached a point where it appears to be the duty and responsibility of the Government either to reveal what it knows, or to order a scientific investigation on a major scale and report the findings immediately to the public at large.*
>
> — *John G. Fuller*

CHAPTER 10

SOME CONCLUDING REMARKS

Appraising an Hypothesis

It is quite appropriate on logical grounds, even an indispensable technique, for an investigator to use any hypothesis that appears to him to help clear up some complex problem. An inquiry can then be undertaken from the perspective afforded by the new hypothesis that is tentatively assumed to be true. By clearing the mind of stale issues, the new mental attitude suggests many fresh questions whose answers may be quite revealing. If the inquiry founders in confusion, then the hypothesis is judged to be useless and another one must be adopted. On the other hand, if the hypothesis brings some order where chaos once prevailed, it is judged to be meritorious. By dispelling confusion and illuminating a complex subject, an hypothesis earns the right to credibility until another one proves to do a better job.

It was taken as fact that some kind of unexplained phenomenon was responsible for the production of UFO reports. That article of faith was based upon a reliability analysis of some reports, the experience of the Air Force for two decades, the scholarly work at the University of Colorado, and the scientific studies of an expert. Given the existence of UFOs, the burden of the next step was to discover a method of penetrating to a deeper understanding of their mysteries. As the personal experiences of witnesses is the only source of information on UFOs, it was felt that their reports should be scrutinized without bias. Upon accepting the validity of the reports, at least temporarily, every effort was made to discover what the witnesses had in mind and to understand their experiences in terms of modern knowledge in all fields. Any individual report is bound to be fragmentary, but the points omitted will not always be the same in all accounts. The full story is expected to emerge as the clues are assembled from many different sightings. Because of the enormous number of reports and their origin from various cultures around the world, the accidental inclusion of some hoaxes and misunderstandings should not grossly distort the final results. Simply stated, the hypothesis was that,

Witnesses tell the truth.

From the way so many inexplicable observations have fallen into consistent patterns in the previous chapters, one must judge this hypothesis to be quite valuable. In addition to improving the coherence of a very broad subject, it has led into many new avenues of investigation that can be verified or denied by experiment. An impressive finding, also, was that the witnesses, having no knowledge of theoretical physics, describe a composite flight pattern of UFOs that is thoroughly in accord with the logical demands of General Relativity. Until another hypothesis has been shown to be more productive, UFO reports should be considered as sincere attempts by people to describe personal experiences, no matter how bizarre they may seem. Future psychological studies can then be relieved of explaining any diabolical motives of the witnesses and can concentrate upon analyzing the irrational skepticism that infects society.

Skeptics Recycle

If the concept of metallic vehicles in the atmosphere displaying an advanced technology is a source of mental anguish, an important point may have been missed somewhere along the way.

Doubts, at this juncture, that people from outer space are visiting the earth may reveal more of an emotional rejection than a rational conclusion. Perhaps by starting again at the beginning of this book and progressing very carefully, the specific problem can be isolated and resolved. Whenever a discussion seems to be too bare or vague, perusual of the references may help. These sources can add immeasurably to the detail of the UFO observations that have been necessarily much abbreviated in the text. The cited literature can also amplify any technical points that may be obscure or unfamiliar.

Improper Questions

"Where do they come from?" "I don't know." This common exchange achieves little but to close the door to fruitful inquiry. The problem is that the question demands either a complete answer or an admission of ignorance. Much more progress can be made when the question admits of intermediate knowledge, such as, "Do the data contain any clues to conditions in their home-land?" The appropriate answer is "Yes, indeed, many." And one is launched on a productive line of research in finding these clues. At the present stage of knowledge none of them has led to unequivocal conclusions. Some are even saddled with implications that are in conflict. Nevertheless, continued research should clarify these points and permit a rather definitive specification of the physical environment from whence the visitors come. Then a parallel study of the cosmos should pinpoint a number of candidate locations where such conditions prevail. If the UFO people live outside our solar system—a possibility that must not be overlooked—then this step may be most difficult, particularly in view of the estimated millions of habitable planets within our galaxy.[1] At any rate, the clues have been seen to appear in considerable variety. Recognizing a dwarf race suggested the corresponding evolutionary conditions of restricted nutrition and limited range of habitation, with possible high temperature and humidity. Breathing of air clearly established dependence upon oxygen, whose partial pressure must be roughly equivalent to that on earth. Nocturnal habits and large, glowing eyes imply low levels of light. Regarding the strength of gravity, several different clues were noted—manner of movement, agility, skinny bodies, and flying suits. These hints led to conflicting interpretations, but the more convincing evidence points to a gravity stronger than that on earth. Continuation of this line of study should produce some interesting results.

"Why haven't they made contact?" This question presupposes that no contact has been made, or that the questioner has not heard of any. While it is clear from the data that association with humanity is generally avoided, it is equally clear that numerous contacts have occurred. They all seemed to have been accidental, and none has lead to interviews on TV or to personal appearances before scientific conventions. It is entirely possible that contacts have been established at high levels of government, as has been claimed. Why there have been no official announcements or denials is about as puzzling as why most governments of the world invoke security measures on information pertaining to this subject, while claiming that it does not officially exist.[2] In any research, the importance of establishing direct communication with the UFO people cannot be overemphasized, for they could readily answer all these perplexing questions.

A Program Plan

Not only is a strong desire a prerequisite to success, one must also know how to proceed toward a particular goal. Ample reason has been offered to justify research on UFOs, and it seems appropriate here to describe a suitable research program. The strategy of this plan is to approach financial commitments gradually, as in a game of stud poker, where for a nominal ante, a few cards may be seen and evaluated. A further bet is required only when the player chooses to stay in the game. His option at any time, of course, is to drop out. So it is with the present plan. It is divided into phases so that the initial investment, or ante, can be minimal; and subsequent risks can be taken from positions of increased knowledge and assurance. The decision to proceed into the next phase would be contingent upon the success of the previous one and the expected benefits of continuing. A corollary strategy is for the overall program to be self-steering. Rather than start an entire program with a rigid plan, at the outset only the first phase is defined in depth while later phases are defined merely in outline. The details would be filled in as work progresses.

Phase I is designed *to confirm absolutely the existence of UFOs in scientific terms and to identify any advanced technologies that may be in use for propulsion or other purposes.* Previous attempts at analyzing the UFO phenomenon have been badly frustrated by the task of cross-correlating the enormous volume of recorded data. As has been emphasized before, the data must be stored in a computer to speed up the search for critical information.[3] A data bank of UFO information, therefore, must become the heart of Phase I. The initial collection of cases to be logged in the computer should be the catalog of close-encounters that has proven to be so helpful in this book, because the breadth of information contained in that collection far exceeds any other of comparable size.[4] Other compilations would be required for studies such as geographical and temporal correlations, flight characteristics, and electromagnetic interference. Much sophistication will be required of the computer programs. In effect, they must have an essentially unlimited ability to search for correlations. At the beginning, no investigator can be clever enough to foresee all the possible correlations. In the previous chapters, the need for new information was seen to arise concerning relationships that had not previously been suspected. Take, for example, the question—"Are helmets worn predominantly during the daytime?" Or another: "Is there a correlation between the weapon used by the UFO people, the color of its beam, and the impact upon the target?" These came up in light of answers to prior questions. The point is that new insights will stimulate new questions. The computer software must also be a masterpiece of flexibility, because the routine scanning of files is not at all sufficient. The equipment must be able to handle language with all its nuances. Through a file of synonyms, it must select cases in which the same phenomena are being described in different words and phrases. It must present the text of case summaries on a cathode ray tube either upon demand, or when a case is identified in correlation searches performed internally. On call, it must display the actual language of the witnesses and technical details of the sighting. Numerical data must be marshalled, processed, and displayed in a great variety of graphical formats. Such software, under development for at least a decade, is currently in usable form at only one place.[5]

A Central Research Team would consist of 6 to 10 people who are broadly knowledgeable and inquisitive, professionally trained in technical fields, and already experts on UFOs. With vastly improved access to the source materials, they would utilize the computer and the methods that have been illustrated here to bring every point up the highest level of documentation. They would push into the frontiers which have been left unexplored, searching for new insights and answers. A staff of experts would provide technical guidance and assure that the work met professional standards in all fields. These consultants would be selected primarily on their qualifications, including a thorough acquaintance with the UFO literature and notable openmindedness, for educating them would be too time-consuming and costly. A few devil's advocates on the staff, however, would be stimulating, and perhaps essential. Consultants would not be required full-time, but their contributions would encompass:

Engineering	Life Sciences	Theory
Electrical	Biology	Evolution
Electronic	Medicine	Exobiology
Automotive	Neurophysiology	Physics
Microwave	Pharmacology	General Relativity
Aeronautical	Opthamology	Unified Field
Chemical	Psychiatry	Mathematical Analysis
Spectroscopy		
Plasma		

Another fundamental feature of Phase I is an experimental program centered at a microwave laboratory in which the standard equipment is augmented by several powerful radar sets. Specific experiments should be performed to measure the effects of microwave energy upon:

Group a)	Automobile lamp filaments, distributor points, speedometers, batteries, and compasses,
Group b)	Radio, television, and telephone circuits,
Group c)	Plunger, inductance, and solid state relays used in the transmission of electrical power,
Group d)	The stimulation of light from atmospheric gases,
Group e)	The production of "low-temperature" plasmas in the atmosphere and the associated chemical processes,
Group f)	The transfer of momentum to atmospheric gases and the production of life upon UFO models, and,
Group g)	Human and animal bodies, such as heating, shock, and paralysis.

A general appraisal at the end of Phase I, including a dominant role by the source of financing, would identify its successes and failures. Final reports would describe the research accomplishments and present a detailed plan for Phase II, if continuation appeared to be justified. The general concept of Phase I is illustrated in an accompanying diagram. (A word of caution: It is not an organization chart.) To save time and administrative costs, primary responsibility for this research should be assigned to a large organization that already has the required staff and facilities.

Now to Phase II. Its character and purpose are essentially different from Phase I. In the event of success in Phase I, *the task of Phase II would be to define the new technology and its potential applications.* Efforts would greatly increase in converting to computer language the many thousands of sighting reports that are already on record. By 1972, some 30,000 cases had been reduced to magnetic tape and are "available for sophisticated analysis.''[6] A liaison office would coordinate the collection of UFO information on a world-wide basis through the United Nations. This office would also manage the flow of information from domestic sources such as the Air Force, the intelligence community, the commercial airlines, civilian groups with active investigators in the field, local police and firemen, and the public at large. New cases arising from these sources would be deposited in the data bank, and a limited number of the most promising ones would be investigated by another office of the program. Teams of specialists, stationed at strategic locations in the United States, and hopefully elsewhere, would fly to the scenes of important sightings with instruments to assist in the *ex post facto* investigation, and with some luck, to witness, measure, and photograph any repeat appearances. As the needs were confirmed, the technical areas previously handled by consultants would be expanded into working departments with defined missions of research and their own laboratory facilities. Each department would maintain direct, hands-on contact with the computerized information center through its own remote terminal. Work of the in-house departments would be supplemented by assignments to subcontractors through the normal practice of issuing invitations for research proposals, evaluating those received, and awarding contracts. A diagram illustrating the concept of Phase II is presented in the following pages.

Let me give some idea of the magnitude envisioned for this work. It appears likely that Phase I could be adequately conducted in about one year with a modest budget of about $4,000,000. Phase II, being substantially more complex and ambitious, would require at least three years and a budget of $75- to $100-million. Thereafter, it is anybody's guess, but the follow-on program would surely emulate the methods that have been so successfully employed in developing nuclear power, intercontinental ballistic missiles, and the Apollo spacecraft.

Let's get started!

PHASE I — VERIFICATION OF CONCEPTS

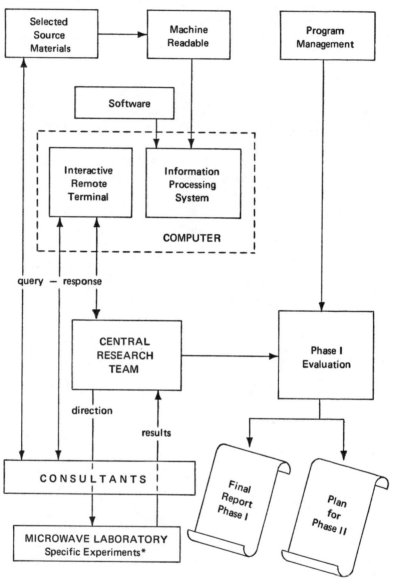

*See Text.

PHASE II — TECHNOLOGY DEFINITION

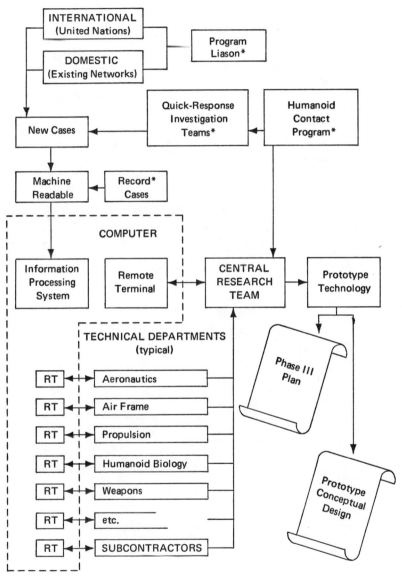

*Activities that might be started early.

Chapter 1: Certified UFOs

1. See article, "Reliability of Equipment and Bibliography, *McGraw-Hill Encyclopedia of Science and Technology*, Vol 11, p. 471, 1971.

2. Olsen, Thomas M., Editor, *The Reference For Outstanding UFO Sighting Reports*, UFO Information Retrieval Center, Inc., Riderwook, Maryland, November, 1966.

3. For example, a comprehensive history may be found in the following book although the author apparently concluded that the golden era of UFOs had come to an end about 1970. Flammonde, Paris, *The Age of Flying Saucers, Notes on a Projected History of Unidentified Flying Objects*, Hawthorn, 1971.

4. In 1969, the American Association for the Advancement of Science resolved that the Blue Book files should be preserved and forwarded a recommendation to that effect to the Secretary of the Air Force.

5. Ruppelt, Edward J., *The Report on Unidentified Flying Objects*, Ace, p. 275 ff, 1956. It is also enlightening to examine the formerly classified reports issued by Blue Book in United States Air Force, *Projects Grudge and Blue Book Reports* 1-12,, assembled and republished by National Investigations Committee on Aerial Phenomena, 1968.

6. The annual breakdown of Blue Book evaluations from 1953 through 1965 were tabulated in Condon, Edward U., *Scientific Study of Unidentified Flying Objects*, p. 521, Dutton, 1969.

7. Condon, Edward U., *Scientific Study of Unidentified Flying Objects*, p. 1, Dutton, 1969.

8. Condon, Edward U., *Scientific Study of Unidentified Flying Objects*, p. 407, Dutton, 1969.

9. Condon, Edward U.,*Scientific Study of Unidentified Flying Objects*, p. 265, Dutton, 1969.

10. Condon, Edward U., *Scientific Study of Unidentified Flying Objects*, p. 270, Dutton, 1969.

11. Hynek, J. Allen, *The UFO Experience-A Scientific Inquiry*, p. 179, Regnery, 1972.

12. *Symposium on Unidentified Flying Objects*, Hynek, J. Allen, Statement to the Committee on Science and Astronautics, U.S. House of Representatives, Ninetieth Congress, p. 4, U.S. Government Printing Office, July 29, 1968.

13. Hynek, J. Allen, "Flying Saucers—Are They Real?" *The Saturday Evening Post*, December 17, 1966.

14. Hynek, J. Allen, "UFO's Merit Scientific Study," Letter to *Science*, 21, October, 1966.

15. *Symposium on Unidentified Flying Objects*, Hynek, J. Allen, Statement to the Committee on Science and Astronautics, U.S. House of Representatives, Ninetieth Congress, p. 14, U.S. Government Printing Office, July 29, 1968.

16. Hynek, J. Allen, "The Earth, The Solar System, and the Cosmos;"

Unidentified Flying Objects, Session II: UFO Reports, Audiotape Program, 136th Meeting, American Association for the advancement of Science, December, 1969. Transcript published in *UFOs, A Scientific Debate,* Sagan, C. and Page, T., Editors, Cornell University Press, 1972.
17. Hynek, J. Allen, *The UFO Experience, A Scientific Inquiry,* Regency, 1972.

CHAPTER 2: *The Vehicles*

1. Shepard, Roger N., "Some Psychological Techniques For The Scientific Investigation of Unidentified Aerial Phenomena," *Symposium on Unidentified Flying Objects,* Hearings before the Committee on Science and Astronautics, U.S. House of Representatives, Ninetieth Congress, Second Edition, p. 226, U.S. Government Printing Office, July 29, 1968.
2. Keyhoe, Donald E., *Flying Saucers From Outer Space,* p. 31, Holt, 1953.
3. Project Grudge Report No. 102-AC-49/15-100, U.S. Air Force, 1949, quoted in Hall, Richard H., Editor, *The UFO Evidence,* p. 143, National Investigations Committee on Aerial Phenomena, 1964.
4. Hall, Richard H., Editor, *The UFO Evidence,* p. 143, National Investigations Committee on Aerial Phenomena, 1964.
5. Data extracted from case summaries in Vallee, Jacques, *Passport to Magonia,* p. 273 ff, Regnery, 1969. Considering synonyms as indicated by the "equal" marks, the selected categories and the number of instances assigned to them were:

* Disc = round	31
Egg = oval	7
Cylinder = cigar = elongated = fuselage	13
Hemisphere = dome = helmet	5
* Plate = saucer	5
* Lip-to-lip dishes	4
Cone	2
Sphere	3
Mushroom	3
Top	1
Lampshade	1

* These categories were all considered to be discs.

6. Shepard, Roger N., "Some Psychological Techniques For The Scientific Investigation of Unidentified Aerial Phenomena," *Symposium on Unidentified Flying Objects,* Hearings before the Committee on Science and Astronautics, U.S. House of Representatives, Ninetieth Congress, Second Edition, p. 232, U.S. Government Printing Office, July 29, 1968.
7. *Complete Directory of UFOs, An Illustrated History of Unexplained Sightings From Project Blue Book, The Official Guide to UFOs,* p. 47, Science and Mechanics Publishing Company, 1968.
8. Personal communication.

9. Missouri UFO Still on the Scene, *UFO Investigator*, p. 2, National Investigations Committee on Aerial Phenomena, May, 1973.
10. Hewes, Hayden C., *Earthprobe*, published by International UFO Bureau, P.O. Box 1281, Oklahoma City, Oklahoma 73101, 1973.
11. San Francisco *Chronicle*, September 30, 1972.
12. Vallee, Jacques, *Passport To Magonia*, p. 24, Regnery, 1969.
13. Hall, Richard E., Editor, *The UFO Evidence*, p. 145., National Investigations Committee on Aerial Phenomena, 1964.
14. Vallee, Jacques, *Passport to Magonia*, Appendix Cases 644, 812, and 902, Regnery, 1969.

Chapter 3: Composition and Luminosity

1. Vallee, Jacques, *Passport to Magonia*, "Appendix A, Century of UFO Landings, 1868 to 1968," Regnery, 1969. Individual events in this catalog are hereafter referred to solely by case number, as in Case 438.
2. Lorenzen, Coral E., *Flying Saucers, The Startling Evidence of The Invasion From Outer Space*, Chapter 9, Signet, 1966.
3. Condon, Edward U., *Scientific Study of Unidentified Flying Objects*, p. 97, Dutton, 1969.
4. Saunders, David R., and Harkins, R. Roger, *UFOs? YES! Where The Condon Committee Went Wrong*, p. 170, Signet, 1968.
5. Peaslee, D.C. and Mueller, H., *Elements of Atomic Physics*, Prentice Hall, 1955.
6. Case 486.
7. Case 848.
8. Harnwell, Gaylord P., *Principles of Electricity and Electromagnetism*, Second Edition, p.85, McGraw-Hill, 1949.
9. Herzberg, Gerhard, *Atomic Spectra and Atomic Structure*, Dover, 1944.
10. Case 541.
11. Case 349.
12. *McGraw-Hill Encyclopedia of Science and Technology*, 1971.
13. *Handbook of Chemistry and Physics*, Chemical Rubber Company, 1969.
14. *Handbook of Chemistry and Physics*, Chemical Rubber Company, 1971.
15. Besancon, Robert M., Editor, *The Encyclopedia of Physics*, p. 743, Reinhold, 1966.
16. Lengyel, Bela A., *Lasers*, Wiley-Interscience, 1971.
17. Bennet, W.R., et al, "Dissociation Excitation Transfers and Optical Maser Oscillations in Ne-Ox and Ar-Ox It Discharges," *Phys. Rev. Letters*, 8, 470-473, 1962.
18. *Handbook of Chemistry and Physics*, Chemical Rubber Company, p. 1,631, 1937.
19. *Encyclopedia of Science and Technology*, Vol. 7, p. 574, McGraw-Hill, 1971.
20. Uman, Martin A., *Lightning*, "Appendix C, Ball Lightning," p. 243, McGraw-Hill, 1969.

21. Cases 560, 601, 613, 733, 737, and probably 776.
22. Klass, Phillip J., *UFOs-Identified*, Random House, 1968.
23. Singer, Stanley, *The Nature of Ball Lightning*,'' Plenum, *1971*.
24. Neville, Roy G., et al, "Microwaves," *Kirk-Othmer Encyclopedia of Chemical Technology*, Supplement Volume, 2nd Edition, pp 563589, Wiley, 1971.
25. Goerz, D.J., *Industrial Microwaves Today*, Bechtel.
26. Baddour, R.F., and Timmins, R.S., eds., *The Application of Plasmas to Chemical Processing*, MIT, 1967.
27. Klass, Phillip J., *UFOs-Identified*, p. 151, Random House, 1968.
28. Lorenzen, Coral E., *Flying Saucers, The Startling Evidence of The Invasion From Outer Space, p. 148, Signet, 1966*.
29. Case 584.
30. Also see descriptions in Cases 282, 309, 310, 316, 322, 339 and 366.
31. Edwards, Frank, *Flying Saucers-Serious Business*, Photograph section, Bantam, 1966.
32. Latimer, Wendell M. and Hildebrand, Joel H., *Reference Book of Inorganic Chemistry*, Revised Edition, p. 181, Macmillan, 1940.
33. *Encyclopedia Britannica*, Vol. 20, p. 822, 1965.
34. Uman, Martin A., *Lightning*, p. 245, McGraw-Hill, 1969.
35. Grey, D.C. and Jensen, M.L., "Bacteriogenic Sulphur in Air Pollution," *Science*, Vol. 177, p. 1099, 22 September 1972.
36. Cases 74 and 199.
37. Neville, Roy G., et al, "Microwaves," *Kirk-Othmer Encyclopedia of Chemical Technology*, Supplement Volume, 2nd Edition, pp 563589, Wiley, 1971.
38. Michel, Aime, *The Truth About Flying Saucers*, p. 143, Pyramid, 1967. The relationship between color change and UFO power was vaguely noted even earlier, see Keyhoe, Donald E., *Flying Saucers From Outer Space*, p. 52, Holt, 1953.
39. Case 670.
40. Case 692, quoted from the original source.
41. Case 741.
42. Case 772.
43. Case 682.
44. Case 821.
45. Case 826.
46. Manufactured by Energy Systems, Inc., Palo Alto, California, according to Leinwoll, Stanley, *Understanding Lasers and Masers*, Rider, 1965.
47. Cases 675 and 575.
48. Case 684.
49. Case 836.
50. Case 796.
51. Case 789.
52. Case 619.

Chapter 4: Sounds

1. Vallee, Jacques, *Passport to Magonia,* Regenery, 1969.
2. Case 677.
3. Shaw, Frank R., and Whitehead, Stanley B., *Honey Bees and Their Management,* Van Nostrand, 1951.
4. Terres, John K., *Flashing Wings, The Drama of Bird Flight,* p. 63, Doubleday, 1968.
5. *Digest of the 1961 International Conference on Medical Electronics,* New York, IRE.
6. Copson, David A., "Microwave Heating, In Freeze-Drying, Electronic Ovens, and Other Applications," Chapter 19, *Radiation Biology of Microwaves,* The AVI Publishing Company, 1962.
7. Taylor, Denise, *Introduction to Radar and Radar Techniques,* Philosophical Library, 1966.
8. *Encyclopedia Americana,* Vol. 23, p. 115a, 1971.
9. *Encyclopedia Britannica,* Vol. 8, p. 215, 1965.
10. Richter, et al, *Noise Reduction of Turbojet Engines,* SNECMA, French manufacturer of jet engines, bi-lingual text.
11. Personal communication, Black & Decker Manufacturing Company, 1139 Airport Boulevard, South San Francisco, California.
12. Richter, et al, *Noise Reduction of Turbojet Engines,* SNECMA.
13. Case 524.
14. Fuller, John G., *The Interrupted Journey,* p. 33, Dell, 1966.
15. Fuller, John G., *The Interrupted Journey,* p. 159, Dell, 1966.
16. Case 902.
17. Condon, Edward U., *Scientific Study of Unidentified Flying Objects,* Case 42, Dutton, 1969. Much more detail on this case is given by Norton, Roy, "World's Most Incredible UFO Contact Case," *Saga,* p. 23-ff, April 1970.

Chapter 5: Electrical Interference

1. Hall, Richard H., Editor, *The UFO Evidence,* National Investigations Committee on Aerial Phenomena, Section VIII, May 1964. Individual cases from this source are designated by the case numbers prefixed by the word Hall.
2. Originally reported in Michel, Aime, *Flying Saucers and the Straight Line Mystery,* p. 143, Criterian, 1958.
3. Case 896.
4. Condon, Edward U., *Scientific Study of Unidentified Flying Objects,* conducted by the University of Colorado, p. 100, Dutton, 1969.
5. Saunders, David R. and Harkins, R. Roger, *UFOs? YES! Where the Condon Committee Went Wrong,* New American Library, 1968.
6. This obscure point came to the author's attention a few years ago and, unfortunately, all efforts to locate the source have been unavailing.
7. Hall, Case 69, p. 75.
8. Dodge, H. S., *RDT, A Radio Guide to Marine Beacons, Aeronautical Beacons, and Broadcast Stations,* Steve Dodge Marine Electronics, Richmond, California, 1964.

9. Local Aeronautical Chart, San Francisco, U.S. Department of Commerce, Coast and Geodetic Survey.
10. Terman, Frederick Emmons, *Fundamentals of Radio,* McGraw-Hill, 1938.

11. Hall, Case 67, p. 75.
12. Hampel, Clifford A., Editor, *Rare Metals Handbook,* 2nd Edition, p. 593, Reinhold.
13. In an alternate design, the heat is supplied by a separate tungsten filament inside a cylindrical cathode.
14. Fuller, John G., *Incident At Exeter,* p. 220, Putnam, 1966.
15. Fuller, John G., *Incident At Exeter,* p. 199, Putnam, 1966.
16. Condon, Edward U., *Scientific Study of Unidentified Flying Objects,* p. 112, Dutton, 1969.
17. McDonald, James E., Prepared Statement, Hearings Before the Committee on Science and Astronautics, U.S. House of Representatives, p. 79, July 29, 1968.
18. Lorenzen, Coral and Jim, *UFOs The Whole Story,* p. 152, Signet, 1969.
19. Fuller, John G., *Incident at Exeter,* p. 207, Putnam, 1966.

Chapter 6: Physiological Effects

1. The primary source for this chapter is Vallee, Jacques, *Passport to Magonia,* Regnery, 1969, referred to merely by case number, in this instance, Case 694.
2. Case 903.
3. Lore, Gordon, *Strange Effect From UFOs,* p. 16, National Investigations Committee on Aerial Phenomena, 1969.
4. Keyhoe, Donald E., *The Flying Saucer Conspiracy,* Holt, 1955.
5. Hall, Richard E., *The UFO Evidence,* National Investigations Committee on Aerial Phenomena, p. 97, 1964.
6. Cases 199, 274, and 358.
7. Case 558.
8. Case 480.
9. Cases 477, 613, 142, 182, 823, 905, and 912.
10. Case 823.
11. Case 650.
12. Cases 482, 524, 720, 906, 912.
13. Lore, Gordon, *Strange Effects From UFOs,* p. 8, National Investigations Committee on Aerial Phenomena, 1969.
14. Cases 274 and 314.
15. Hall, Richard E., *The UFO Evidence,* p. 97, National Investigations Committee on Aerial Phenomena, 1964,
16. Cases 682 and 524.
17. Case 300.
18. Case 525.
19. Case 323.
20. Case 413.

21. Case 337.
22. Bukstein, Edward J., *Medical Electronics,* p. 131, Ungar, 1959.
23. Copson, David A., "Microwave Heating—In Freeze-Drying, Electronic Ovens, and Other Applications," Chapter 19, *Radiation Biology of Microwaves,* AVI Publishing Co., 1962.
24. *Encyclopedia Britannica,* Vol. 16, p. 38, 1965.
25. Fitzhugh, Richard, "Mathematical Models of Excitation and Propogation In Nerve," Chapter I, Schwan, Herman P., Editor, *Biological Engineering, McGraw-Hill, 1969.*
26. Copson, David A., "Microwave Heating—In FreezeDrying Electronic Ovens, and Other Applications," Chapter 19, *Radiation Biology of Microwaves,* AVI Publishing Co., 1962.
27. Fitzhugh, Richard, "Mathematical Models of Excitation and Propagation in Nerve," Chapter I. Schwan, Herman P., Editor, *Biological Engineering,* McGraw-Hill, 1969.
28. Case 402.
29. Leavell, Lutie, C., et al., *Anatomy and Physiology, 15th* Edition, p. 239, MacMillan, 1966.
30. Reynolds, Martin R., "Development of a Garment for Protection of Personnel in High-Power RF Environments," Peyton, Mary Fouse, Editor, *Biological Effects of Microwave Radiation, Proceedings of the Fourth Annual Tri-Service Conference,* p. 71, Vol. 1, 16-18 August 1960, New York University, Plenum Press, 1961.
31. Payne, James N., "Similarities and Differences Between Technical Aspects of the Navy HERO Program for Ordnance and the Personnel Hazard Program," Peyton, Mary Fouse, Editor, *Biological Effects of Microwave Radiation, Proceedings of the Fourth Annual Tri-Service Conference,* p. 319, Vol. 1, 16-18 August 1960, New York University, Plenum Press, 1961.
32. Finch, Bernard E., "Phosphenes and the UFO Phenomenon," *Flying Saucer Review,* Vol. 16, No. 5, p. 9, September/October, 1970.
33. Case 662, original source.
34. Case 900.
35. Milroy, William C., and Michaelson, Sol M., "Biological Effects of Microwave Radiation," *Health Physics,* Vol. 20, p. 570, Pergamon Press, June 1971.
36. Case 677.
37. Neville, Roy G., et al., "Microwaves," *Kirk-Othmer Encyclopedia of Chemical Technology,* p. 585, Wiley, 1971.
38. Case 000.
39. Case 893.
40. Milroy, William C., and Michaelson, Sol M., "Biological Effects of Microwave Radiation," *Health Physics,* Vol, 20, p. 573, Pergamon Press, June 1971.
41. Michaelson, "Sol M., and Dodge, Christopher H., Soviet Views on the Biological Effects of Microwaves—An Analysis," *Health Physics,* Vol. 21, p. 108, Pergamon Press, July 1971.

42. Gordon, Z. V., *Biological Effects of Microwaves in Occupational Hygiene,* Translated From Russian, National Aeronautics and Space Administration, Israel Program for Scientific Translations, 1970, available from Clearinghouse for Federal and Technical Information, Springfield, Va. 22151.
43. Wade, Nicholas, "Fischer-Spassky Charges: What Did The Russians Have In Mind?" *Science,* Vol. 177, p. 778, 1 September 1972.
44. Cases 484, 485, 540, 835, and 908.
45. Cases 748 and 895.
46. Case 697.
47. Case 755.
48. Case 590.
49. Case 629.
50. Case 787.
51. Case 525.
52. Case 616.
53. Case 529.
54. Case 581.
55. Case 588.
56. Case 592.
57. Case 706.
58. Case 778.
59. Cases 551, 678, 754, 855, 871, 873, 877, 910, and 913.
60. Fuller, John G., *Incident At Exeter,* p. 143, Putnam, 1966.
61. This impression is inescapable in view of quotations from Fuller, John G., *Incident At Exeter,* pages 63, 65, 71, 72, 73, 81, 133, 143, 175, 176, 177, and 181, Putnam, 1966.
62. A "New FSR Catalogue, The Effects of UFOs Upon Animals, Birds, and Smaller Creatures," *Flying Saucer Review,* beginning in Vol. 16, No. 1, January/February 1970. Subsequent references in this section are identified as FSR Case NK,
63. FSR Case 34.
64. FSR Case 62.
65. FSR Case 118.
66. FSR Case 120.
67. FSR Case 30.
68. FSR Case 34.
69. FSR Case 71.
70. FSR Case 72.
71. FSR Case 44.
72. FSR Case 78.
73. FSR Case 37.
74. Milroy, William C., and Michaelson, Sol M., "Biological Effects of Microwave Radiation," *Health Physics,* pp. 567-575, Vol. 20, June 1971.
75. FSR Case 28.
76. FSR Case 31.
77. FSR Case 42.

78. FSR Case 75.
79. FSR Case 23.
80. FSR Case 67.
81. FSR Case 69, original source.
82. FSR Case 75.
83. FSR Case 109.
84. For a compilation of 43 cases involving angel hair see Hall, Richard H., Editor, *The UFO Evidence*, p. 100, National Investigations Committee on Aerial Phenomena, 1964. Regrettably the author can offer no suggestions as to the purpose, composition, or significance of angel hair.
85. FSR Case 116.
86. Vallee, Jacques, *Passport To Magonia*, Cases 187, 222, 639, and 850, Regnery, 1969.
87. Fuller, John G., *Incident at Exeter*, p. 35, Putnam, 1966.

Chapter 7: Flight and Propulsion

1. Hall, Richard, H., *The UFO Evidence*, National Investigation Committee on Aerial Phenomena, 3535 University Blvd., West, Suite 23, Kensington, Maryland 20795, May 1964.
2. Case 484.
3. The context requires this language to mean that the inertial behavior would remain unchanged.
4. Markowitz, William, "The Physics and Metaphysics of Unidentified Flying Objects," *Science*, Vol. 157, p. 1277, 15 September 1967.
5. Nordtvedt, Kenneth L., Jr., "Gravitation Theory; Empirical Status From Solar System Experiments," *Science*, Vol. 178, p. 1157, December 15 1972.
6. Born, Max, et al, *Einstein's Theory of Relativity*, p. 313, Revised Edition, Dover, 1962.
7. Barnett, Lincoln, *The Universe and Dr. Einstein*, p. 71, Times Inc., 1948.
8. Nordtvedt, Kenneth L., Jr., "Gravitation Theory; Empirical Status From Solar System Experiments," *Science*, Vol. 178, 15 December 1972.
9. *Handbook of Chemistry and Physics*, p. 2016, Chemical Rubber Company, 1937.
10. Condon, Edward U., *Scientific Study of Unidentified Flying Objects*, p. 143, Dutton, 1969.
11. Hall, Richard H., *The UFO Evidence*, p. 81, National Investigations Committee on Aerial Phenomena, May 1964.
12. Roach, Franklin E., "Visual Observations Made By U.S. Astronauts," Chapter 6 of Condon, Edward U., *Scientific Study of Unidentified Flying Objects*, Dutton, 1969.
13. Personal communication.
14. Binder, Otto O., "Secret Messages From UFOs," *Saga*, date unknown.
15. *Aviation Week and Space Technology*, 88, p. 21, 1968.
16. *Literature Search No. 541, Interactions of Spacecraft and Other Moving Bodies with Natural Plasmas*, Jet Propulsion Laboratory, 1965.

17. Friedman, Stanton T., *Symposium on Unidentified Flying Objects,* Hearings Before the Committee on Science and Astronautics, U.S. House of Representatives, Hon. J. Edward Roush presiding, p. 217, July 29,. 1968. Also see a more readily available, popular version that, having lost some of the technical detail, is bland and stale in comparison to the original. Fuller, John G., *Aliens In the Skies, The Scientific Rebuttal To the Condon Committee Report,* Putnam, 1969.

18. Cases 72, 223, 288, and 515.

19. Case 93.

20. Case 106.

21. Case 540.

22. Case 499.

23. Cases 228, 321, 414, and 469.

24. Case 469.

25. Case 512.

27. Case 397.

27. Berliner, Don, "The U.F.O. From The Designer's Viewpoint," *Air Progress,* p. 36, October, 1967 from Greif, R.K. and Tolhurst, W.H., *NASA Technical Note D-1432,* Ames Research Center, 1963.

28. Case 88.

29. Cases 81, 96, 148, 348, 521, 529, and 557.

30. Case 375.

31. Case 62.

32. Case 391.

33. Case 398.

34. Case 442.

35. Case 129.

36. Case 388.

37. Case 819.

38. Cases 194 and 358.

39. Case 332.

40. Case 464.

41. Case 832.

42. Case 514.

43. Case 720.

44. Case 211.

45. Leslie, Desmond, and Adamski,George, *Flying Saucers Have Landed.* p. 208, British Book Center, 1953.

46. Case 272.

47. Peres, A., "Motion and Radiation of Pole Particles," p. 361, in *Recent Developments In General Relativity,* Polish Scientific Publishers, 1962.

48. Case 97, original source.

49. Case 378.

50. Case 340.

51. Case 417.

52. Cases 264 and 265.

53. Case 262.

54. Case 292.

55. Case 230.
56. Case 533.
57. Case 627.
58. Case 634.
59. Case 836.
60. Cases 702 and 836.
61. Case 303.
62. Case 745.
63. Case 944.
64. Condon, Edward U., *Scientific Study of Unidentified Flying Objects,* p. 260 ff, Dutton, 1969.
65. McDonald, James E., "Science in Default; Twenty-two Years of Inadequate UFO Investigations," Chapter 5 of Sagan, Carl, and Page, Thornton, Editors, UFOs, *A Scientific Debate,* Cornell, 1972.
66. Bowen, Charles, Editor, "The Humanoids," p. 36, *Flying Saucer Review,* London, 1968.
67. Copson, David A., *Microwave Heating,* p. 410, AVI Publishing Co., 1962.
68. Bergmann, Peter G. and Komar, Arthur B., "Status Report on the Quantization of the Gravitational Field," p. 31, in *Recent Developments In General Relativity,* Polish Scientific Publishers, 1962.

Chapter 8: Plots and Passengers

1. Hynek, J. Allen, *The UFO Experience,* p. 164, Regnery, 1972.
2. Hynek, J. Allen, *The UFO Experience,* Chapter 11, Regnery, 1972.
3. Ruppelt, Edward J., *The Report on Unidentified Flying Objects,* p. 88, Ace, 1956. This book by the officer formerly in charge of UFO investigations by the Air Force is a classic.
4. Vallee, Jacques, *Passport to Magonia,* Regnery, 1972.
5. Hynek, J. Allen, *The UFO Experience,* p. 161, Regnery, 1972.
6. Cases 691, 695, 698, 701, 703, and 705.
7. Case 609.
8. Case 917.
9. *Guinness Book of World Records,* Chapter One, "The Human Being," Bantam, 1971.
10. San Francisco *Chronicle,* p. 1, March 27, 1973.
11. Coon, Charleton S., *The Living Races of Man,* p. 13, Knopf, 1965.
12. Coon, Charleton S., *The Origin of the Races,* p. 12, Knopf, 1963.
13. Compare a sketch prepared by the U.S. Air Force from descriptions of he witnesses to the famous Kelly-Hopkinsville case in Bower, Charles, Editor, "The Humanoids," p. 65, *Flying Saucer Review,* London, 1968 and a picture of a model made from the same sources in Vallee, Jacques, *Passport to Magonia,* Regnery, 1969.
14. *Guinness Book of World Records,* Chapter One, "The Human Being," Bantam, 1971.
15. Case 82.

16. Leslie, Desmond and Adamski, George, *Flying Saucers Have Landed,* p. 94, British Book Center, 1953.
17. Bowen, Charles, Editor, "The Humanoids," Cases 44, 54, and 3, *Flying Saucer Review,* London, 1968.
18. Case 642.
19. Case 289.
20. Case 918.
21. Case 61, original source.
22. Edwards, P. M. H., "Speech of the Aliens," *Flying Saucer Review,* London, January-February and March-April, 1970.
23. Case 877.
24. Bowen, Charles, Editor, "The Humanoids," p. 43, *Flying Saucer Review,* London, 1968.
25. Case 396.
26. Leslie, Desmond, *Flying Saucers Have Landed,* British Book Center, 1953.
27. Case 126.
28. Case 515.
29. Case 443, original source.
30. Vallee, Jacques, *Passport to Magonia,* Regnery, 1969.
31. Case 716.
32. Case 678.
33. Case 804.
34. Case 517.
35. Case 568.
36. Case 596.
37. Case 531.
38. Case 545.
39. Case 767.
40. Case 116, original source.
41. Leslie, Desmond and Adamski, George, *Flying Saucers Have Landed,* p. 196, British Book Center, 1953.
42. Case 812.
43. Case 638.
44. Case 506.
45. Case 617.
46. Case 642.
47. Case 217.
48. Coon, Carleton S., *The Origin of Races,* p. 70, Knopf, 1962.
49. Martin, Paul J., "The Discovery of America," *Science,* Vol. 179, p. 969, 9 March 1973.
50. Case 638.

Chapter 9: Activities on Earth

1. Case 650.
2. Case 701.

3. Case 353.
4. Case 154.
5. Case 327.
6. Case 324.
7. Case 541.
8. Case 596, original source.
9. Case 862.
10. Case 344.
11. Case 353.
12. Case 339.
13. Bowen, Charles, Editor, "The Humanoids," p. 56, *Flying Saucer Review*, London, 1968.
14. Case 430.
15. A "New FSR Catalogue, The Effects of UFOs Upon Animaals, Birds, and Smaller creatures, Cases 57 and 73, *Flying Saucer Review*, beginning in Vol. 16, No. 1, January/February 1970.
16. Lorenzen, Coral and Jim, *Flying Saucer Occupants*. p. 130, Signet, 1967.
17. Case 80.
18. Case 40.
19. Case 501.
20. Case 95.
21. Case 517, original source.
22. Case 918.
23. Case 614.
24. Case 109.
25. Case 327, original source.
26. Case 719.
27. Case 596, original source.
28. Case 338.
29. Case 404.
30. Case 420.
31. Case 816.
32. Case 907.
33. Case 812.
34. Case 238.
35. Case 476.
36. Case 685.
37. Case 812.
38. Case 400.
39. Case 153.
40. Case 762.
41. Case 82.
42. Case 303.
43. Case 844, original source.
44. Case 659.
45. Case 920.
46. Lorenzen, Coral, E., *Flying Saucers, The Startling Evidence of the Invasion From Outer Space*, p. 105, Signet, 1966.

47. Edwards, Frank, *Flying Saucers-Serious Business,* p. 45, Bantam, 1966.
48. Scully, Frank, *Behind the Flying Saucers,* p. 153, Gollancz, London, 1955.
49. Case 860.
50. Case 83, original source.
51. Case 285.
52. Stranges, Frank E., *The Stranger At The Pentagon,* I.E.C., 7070 Woodman Avenue, Van Nuys, California, 1967.
53. Case 394.
54. Case 703.
55. Case 552.
56. Case 305.
57. Cases 370 and 404.
58. Case 396, original source.
59. Case 344, original source.
60. Case 61, original source.
61. Norman, Eric, *This Hollow Earth,* Lancer, 1972.
62. Nourse, Alan E., *Nine Planets,* Appendix I, Pyramid, 1960.
63. McMahon, Thomas, "Size and Shape in Biology," *Science,* Vol. 179, p. 1201, 23 March 1973.
64. Case 874
65. Case 866.
66. Case 885.
67. Case 145.
68. Case 867.
69. Case 865.
70. Case 878, original source.
71. Case 879, original source.
72. Case 915.
73. Case 501.
74. Case 583.
75. Case 857.
76. Case 476.
77. Case 580.
78. Case 767.
79. Fredrickson, Sven Olof, "Finnish Encounter In The Snow," *Flying Saucer Review,* Vol. 16, No. 4, p. 31, July, August 1970, and "A Humanoid Was Seen at Imjarvi," Vol. 16, No. 5, p. 14, September/October, 1970.
80. Case 778.
81. Sanderson, Ivan T., *Invisible Residents,* p. 35, World, 1970.
82. Case 519.
83. Vallee, Jacques and Janine, *Challenge To Science, The UFO Enigma,* p. 174 ff, Ace, 1966.
84. Case 637.
85. Case 624.
86. Case 61, original source.
87. Cases 284 and 700.

88. Vallee, Jacques, "The Pattern Behind The UFO Landings, Humanoids," p. 8, *Flying Saucer Review,* London, 1968.
89. Cases 324, 349, and 804.
90. Case 298.
91. Case 372.
92. Cases 505, 691, and 744.
93. Case 580.
94. Cases 596 and 804.
95. Cases 505 and 588.
96. Case 552.
97. Case 356.
98. Case 650.
99. Case 51.
100. Case 641.
101. Case 95.
102. Cases 97 and 583.
103. Case 311.
104. Case 662.
105. Cases 93, 580, and 638.
106. Case 920.
107. Case 125.
108. Case 95.
109. Case 311.
110. Case 356.
111. Case 583.
112. Case 662.
113. Case 220.
114. Cases 97 and 583.
115. Anderson, Jack, "A Magic Ray Play To Trap Hijackers," San Francisco *Chronicle,* September 21, 1972.
116. Fuller John G., *The Interrupted Journey,* Dell, 1966.
117. Lorenzen, Coral and Jim, *Flying Saucer Occupants,* Chapter III, "Report on The Villa Boas Incident," Signet, 1967.
118. Cases 624, 636, and 706.
119. Case 41.

Chapter 10: Some Concluding Remarks

1. Dole, Stephen H., *Habitable Planets For Man,* Blaisdell, 1964.
2. The question of censorship and classification has been well reported by Lorenzen, Jim and Coral, *UFOs Over The Americas,* Chapter X and Appendices, Signet, 1968.
3. Hynek, J. Allen, *The UFO Experience,* p. 183, Regnery, 1972.
4. Vallee, Jacques, *Passport to Magonia,* Regnery, 1969.
5. Stanford Research Institute, Palo Alto, California.

INDEX

ABOUT THE AUTHOR

Mr. McCampbell served in the Corps of Engineers during World War II as a junior officer and parachutist. Subsequently, he entered the University of California at Berkeley where a broad education culminated in a bachelor's degree in Engineering–Physics. Extensive graduate studies in the following years focused on physics and mathematics. His early career was devoted to applied research on nuclear weapons and the theoretical aspects of designing nuclear reactors for submarines and electric generating stations. During the past decade he has been engaged in technical management. His specialty is planning and managing large-scale projects involving advanced technologies. Major credits include expansion plans for national research centers, economic development plans for foreign nations, test facilities for NASA, and nuclear power stations. He has been recognized in *American Men of Science,* the international *Who's Who in Atoms, Notable Americans of the Bicentennial Eve,* and *Who's Who in America.* Professional affiliations include the American Association for the Advancement of Science and the American Nuclear Society, in which he was elected Chairman for Northern California.

BOOKS OF RELATED INTEREST

Through a series of taped interviews in which two beings in different times and dimensions speak through Lenora Huett, J. H. Mathes writes compellingly in THE AMNESIA FACTOR of what they said about him, about mankind, space, other worlds, and God. 180 pages, soft cover, $4.95

In THE HUMAN DYNAMO, famed parapsychologist Hans Holzer offers precise techniques on how to tune in to a higher power reservoir and how to use it to achieve harmonious and full expression of consciousness on all levels. 128 pages, soft cover, $4.95

In ALPHA BRAIN WAVES, David Boxerman and Aron Spilken analyze the mystery surrounding research into the alpha state and examine the industry that has evolved from it. 128 pages, soft cover, $4.95

In JOURNEY TO THE MOON, Joseph McHugh and Latif Harris skillfully match the ideas of Plato with classic engravings by Gustave Dore to produce a work of art touched with supernatural awe. 96 pages, 41 Dore reproductions, 2-color, 6 x 7½, soft cover, $3.95

In I AM NOT SPOCK, Leonard Nimoy reveals the experiences and adventures he shared with the legendary STAR TREK character he created—Mr. Spock, First Officer of the Starship Enterprise.
"... a most intriguing voyage through inner space..." —New York Times
"... a remarkably pleasant and gentle tale of the only fictional character since Sherlock Holmes to have won the love of millions entirely by being rational..." —Isaac Asimov
"... I AM NOT SPOCK's openness, candor and wit will provide solid, enjoyable reading for any literate, regardless of age." —Grover Sales
152 pages, soft cover, $4.95

CELESTIAL ARTS
Millbrae, California